Virginia
Standards of Learning *Success*

POWERED BY
GO Math!

INCLUDES

- Virginia Standards of Learning Lessons
- Lesson Practice/Homework with Spiral Review

Table of Contents

Name _____

Numbers Through Ten Thousand

Essential Question How can you represent 4-digit numbers in different ways?

Learning Objective You will write whole numbers up to ten thousand using numbers to show the values of ones, tens, hundreds, and thousands.

🔑 Unlock the Problem (Real World)

The ABC Blocks factory makes blocks in three different kinds of packages: boxes of 100 blocks, stacks of 10 blocks, and single blocks. The boxes of 100 blocks are packed into crates that hold 1,000 blocks. How many boxes of 100 blocks are in each crate of 1,000?

- Underline what the problem is asking you to find.
- What number will you count by to find the answer?
  _____

🔑 Count by hundreds to find the total number of boxes of 100 blocks that will go into each crate. Then count the crates.

__100__ __200__ _____ _____ _____ _____ _____ _____ _____ _____

[1] [2] [ ] [ ] [ ] [ ] [ ] [ ] [ ] [ ]

So, there are _____ boxes of 100 blocks in each crate of 1,000.

🔑 Example

ABC Blocks has an order for 2,600 blocks. Suppose the factory has no crates. How many boxes of 100 will it pack?

You know there are 10 boxes of 100 in 1,000,

so there are _____ boxes of 100 in 2,000.

There are _____ boxes of 100 in 600.

Add the boxes. $20 + 6 =$ _____

So, the factory will pack _____ boxes of 100.

Math Talk — Math Processes and Practices ③

Apply What if the factory had crates of 1,000 and stacks of 10, but no boxes of 100? Explain how it could pack the order.

© Houghton Mifflin Harcourt Publishing Company

Try This! Show numbers in different ways.

A When Vince packs orders at ABC Blocks, he likes to use the fewest packages possible. The orders Vince packs are shown below. Complete the chart.

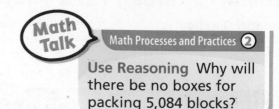
Math Talk

Math Processes and Practices ②

Use Reasoning Why will there be no boxes for packing 5,084 blocks?

Number of Blocks Ordered	Crates (Thousands)	Boxes (Hundreds)	Stacks (Tens)	Single Blocks (Ones)
1,479		4		9
5,084	5			4

B When there are not enough crates, boxes, or stacks to pack the orders, Vince uses a package that is the next smaller size. The chart below shows which packages Vince does not have enough of to pack the orders. Complete the chart.

Number of Blocks Ordered	Crates (Thousands)	Boxes (Hundreds)	Stacks (Tens)	Single Blocks (Ones)
1,479	0			9
5,084		0	0	

C Sometimes Vince draws a quick picture to check his work. This is his drawing for 1,479 blocks. He uses T for thousands, ☐ for hundreds, | for tens, and ○ for ones. Fill in the unknown numbers.

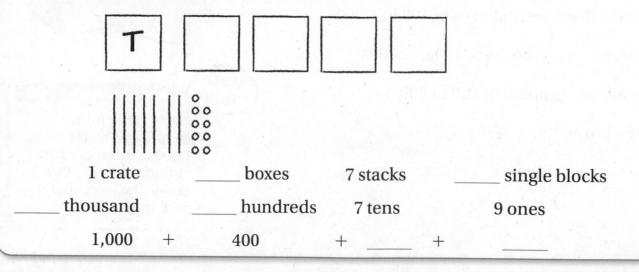

1 crate   _____ boxes   7 stacks   _____ single blocks

_____ thousand   _____ hundreds   7 tens   9 ones

1,000   +   400   +   _____   +   _____

Numbers Through Ten Thousand

Learning Objective You will write whole numbers up to ten thousand using numbers to show the values of ones, tens, hundreds, and thousands.

Complete the packing chart. Use the fewest packages possible.

	Number of Blocks Ordered	Crates (Thousands)	Boxes (Hundreds)	Stacks (Tens)	Single Blocks (Ones)
1.	1,492	1	4	9	2
2.	3,016			1	
3.	2,804				
4.	4,675				

Complete the packing chart. When there is a zero, use the next-smaller size package.

	Number of Blocks Ordered	Crates (Thousands)	Boxes (Hundreds)	Stacks (Tens)	Single Blocks (Ones)
5.	1,727	0		2	7
6.	2,351	1		0	
7.	5,008	0		0	
8.	4,976		29	0	

Problem Solving Real World

9. A worker at the block factory packed blocks in 3 crates of 1,000; 4 boxes of 100; and 9 single blocks. How many blocks did the worker pack?

_____

10. Matt needs to pack an order for 1,816 blocks. How can Matt pack the blocks without using crates of 1,000?

_____

Lesson Check

1. Which could be added to show 2,237?

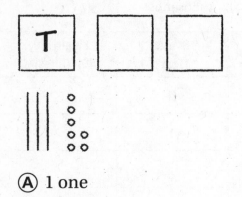

- (A) 1 one
- (B) 1 ten
- (C) 1 hundred
- (D) 1 thousand

2. What number does the quick picture show?

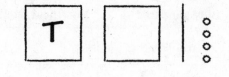

- (A) 1,140
- (B) 1,114
- (C) 1,014
- (D) 114

Spiral Review

3. Which number is NOT even?

- (A) 35
- (B) 36
- (C) 42
- (D) 78

4. Tom thinks of an odd number between 15 and 30. The sum of the digits is 7. What is Tom's number?

- (A) 16
- (B) 17
- (C) 25
- (D) 27

5. Write the number the quick picture shows.

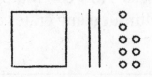

_____

6. Write an addition fact that can help you find the difference.

$16 - 7 = \blacksquare$

_____

Name _____

Numbers Through Hundred Thousands

Essential Question How can you find the value of each digit in a 6-digit number?

Learning Objective You will model and identify the place and value of each digit in a 6-digit number.

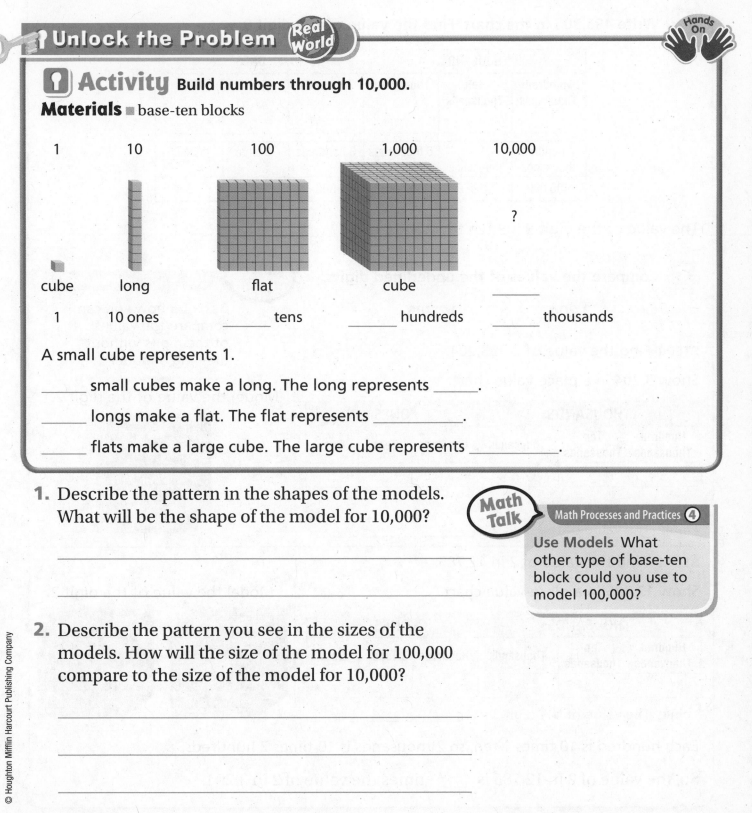

Unlock the Problem Real World

Activity Build numbers through 10,000.

Materials ■ base-ten blocks

1	10	100	1,000	10,000
cube	long	flat	cube	_____
1	10 ones	_____ tens	_____ hundreds	_____ thousands

A small cube represents 1.

_____ small cubes make a long. The long represents _____.

_____ longs make a flat. The flat represents _____.

_____ flats make a large cube. The large cube represents _____.

1. Describe the pattern in the shapes of the models. What will be the shape of the model for 10,000?

   _____

   _____

Math Talk

Math Processes and Practices ④

Use Models What other type of base-ten block could you use to model 100,000?

2. Describe the pattern you see in the sizes of the models. How will the size of the model for 100,000 compare to the size of the model for 10,000?

   _____

   _____

   _____

Value of a Digit The value of a digit depends on its place-value position in the number. A place-value chart can help you understand the value of each digit in a number. The value of each place is 10 times the value of the place to the right.

 Write 496,305 in the chart. Find the value of the digit 9.

THOUSANDS			ONES		
Hundred Thousands	Ten Thousands	Thousands	Hundreds	Tens	Ones
4 hundred thousands	9 ten thousands	6 thousands	3 hundreds	0 tens	5 ones
400,000	90,000	6,000	300	0	5

The value of the digit 9 is 9 ten thousands, or _____.

 Compare the values of the underlined digits.

3,<u>2</u>04   1<u>2</u>,785

STEP 1 Find the value of 2 in 3,204.

Show 3,204 in a place-value chart.

THOUSANDS			ONES		
Hundred Thousands	Ten Thousands	Thousands	Hundreds	Tens	Ones

Think: The value of the digit 2 is _____.

Math Talk

Math Processes and Practices ⑥

Describe how you can compare the values of the digits without drawing a model.

Model the value of the digit 2.

STEP 2 Find the value of 2 in 12,785.

Show 12,785 in a place-value chart.

THOUSANDS			ONES		
Hundred Thousands	Ten Thousands	Thousands	Hundreds	Tens	Ones

Think: The value of the digit 2 is _____.

Model the value of the digit 2.

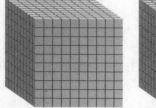

Each hundred is 10 times 1 ten, so 2 thousands is 10 times 2 hundreds.

So, the value of 2 in 12,785 is _____ times the value of 2 in 3,204.

Name _____

1. Complete the table below.

Number	100,000	10,000	1,000	100	10	1
Model	?	?				.
Shape	?	?	cube	flat	long	cube
Group			10 hundreds	10 tens	10 ones	1 one

Find the value of the underlined digit.

2. 7̲03,890

3. 63,54̲0

4. 18̲2,034

✓ **5.** 345̲,890

_____ | _____ | _____ | _____

Compare the values of the underlined digits.

6. 2̲,000 and 2̲00

The value of the digit 2 in _____

is _____ times the value of the

digit 2 in _____ .

✓ **7.** 4̲0 and 4̲00

The value of the digit 4 in _____

is _____ times the value of the

digit 4 in _____ .

On Your Own

Find the value of the underlined digit.

8. 23̲0,001

9. 803̲,040

10. 46,84̲2

11. 9̲80,650

_____ | _____ | _____ | _____

12. Kyle has collected 4,385 buttons and Jenna has collected 3,899 buttons. How can you compare the value of the digit 3 in 4,385 to the value of the digit 3 in 3,899?

_____

_____

13. GO DEEPER Patrick wants to model the number 13,450 using base-ten blocks. How many large cubes, flats, and longs does he need to model the number?

_____

_____

Problem Solving • Applications (Real World)

Use the table for 14.

14. [GO DEEPER] How can you compare the value of the digit 4 in the population of Memphis to the value of the digit 4 in the population of Denver?

_____

_____

15. [THINK SMARTER] How many models of 100 do you need to model 3,200? Explain.

_____

_____

_____

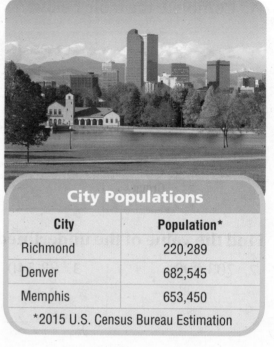

City Populations

City	Population*
Richmond	220,289
Denver	682,545
Memphis	653,450

*2015 U.S. Census Bureau Estimation

16. [Math Processes and Practices 6] Becca wrote 913,405 on her paper. Using numbers and words, **explain** how the number would change if she exchanged the digits in the hundred thousands and tens places.

_____

_____

WRITE ▶ Math • **Show Your Work**

17. [THINK SMARTER] For numbers 17a–17e, select True or False for each statement.

17a. The value of 7 in 375,081 is 7,000.   ○ True   ○ False

17b. The value of 6 in 269,480 is 600,000.   ○ True   ○ False

17c. The value of 5 in 427,593 is 500.   ○ True   ○ False

17d. The value of 1 in 375,081 is 10.   ○ True   ○ False

17e. The value of 4 in 943,268 is 40,000.   ○ True   ○ False

Numbers Through Hundred Thousands

Learning Objective You will model and identify the place and value of each digit in a 6-digit number.

Find the value of the underlined digit.

1. 6,0<u>3</u>5

    30
    _____

2. 43,<u>7</u>82

    _____

3. 506,08<u>7</u>

    _____

4. 4<u>9</u>,254

    _____

5. 1<u>3</u>6,422

    _____

6. 673,<u>5</u>12

    _____

7. <u>8</u>14,295

    _____

8. 73<u>6</u>,144

    _____

Compare the values of the underlined digits.

9. 6,<u>3</u>00 and 5<u>3</u>0

    The value of the digit 3 in _____

    is _____ times the value of the digit 3

    in _____ .

10. <u>2</u>,783 and 7,<u>2</u>83

    The value of the digit 2 in _____

    is _____ times the value of the digit 2

    in _____ .

Problem Solving Real World

Use the table for 11–12.

11. What is the value of the digit 9 in the attendance at the Lions vs. Giants game?

    _____

12. The attendance at which game has a 7 in the ten thousands place?

    _____

Football Game Attendance	
Game	**Attendance**
Lions vs. Giants	69,143
Ravens vs. Titans	73,021
Patriots vs. Dolphins	68,756

13. **WRITE** ▸*Math* How does the value of a digit in the hundred thousands place compare to the value of a digit in the ten thousands place?

    _____

    _____

Lesson Check

1. During one season, the average attendance at a professional football game was 74,086. What is the value of the digit 4 in the number of people?

2. Clayton forgot the number of people at the football game. He does remember that the number had five digits and a 3 in the hundreds place. Write a number that Clayton could be thinking of.

Spiral Review

3. Benjamin uses 2 quarters, 4 dimes, and 1 nickel to buy a kite. How much money does he use?

4. Jasmine has 78 stickers. Martin has 19 fewer stickers than Jasmine. How many stickers does Martin have?

5. The clock below shows the time when Carly leaves her home for school. At what time does Carly leave home?

6. Two pictures are the same size. A third of one picture is black and a fourth of the other picture is gray. Is the black part or the gray part larger?

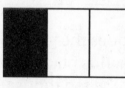 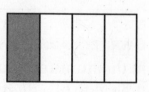

Name _____

Read and Write Numbers Through Hundred Thousands

Essential Question What are some ways you can read and write numbers?

Lesson Objective You will read and write 6-digit whole numbers in standard, expanded, and word form.

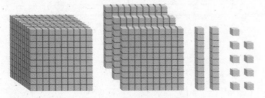

ABC Blocks receives an order. The base-ten blocks show the number of blocks ordered.

- How many blocks were ordered?

_____

Math Idea

The location of a digit in a number tells its value.

Each worker on a team checks the order by expressing the number in a different way. What way does each worker use?

Word form is a way to write a number using words.

Expanded form is a way to write a number by showing the value of each digit.

Standard form is a way to write a number using the digits 0 to 9, with each digit having a place value.

Sam gets the order and reads the number to Mary.

one thousand, three hundred twenty-nine

Mary uses the value of each digit to record the number of blocks that will be in each type of package.

1,000 + 300 + 20 + 9

When the order is complete, Kyle writes the total number of blocks on the packing slip.

1,329

So, Sam says the number using _____ form,

Mary uses _____ form, and Kyle

uses _____ form.

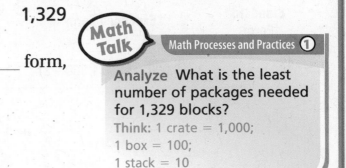

Math Talk

Math Processes and Practices ①

Analyze What is the least number of packages needed for 1,329 blocks?

Think: 1 crate = 1,000;
1 box = 100;
1 stack = 10

Try This! Complete the chart to show three forms of the number.

Standard Form	Expanded Form	Word Form
5,742		five thousand, _____ hundred _____
		one hundred two thousand, ninety-one
	10,000 + 3,000 + 600 + 7	_____ thousand, _____ hundred seven

Share and Show MATH BOARD

1. Complete the expanded form for 6,295.

_____ + 200 + 90 + _____

Math Talk

Math Processes and Practices ②

Use Reasoning Why is 62 hundreds 9 tens 5 ones equal to 6,295?

Use the model to write the number in three ways.

✓ **2.**

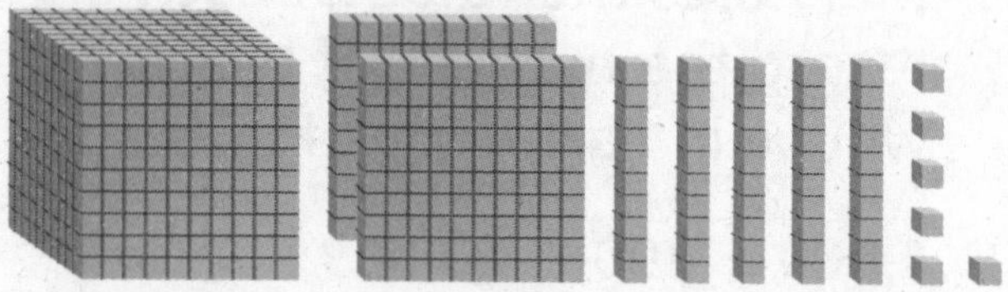

Standard Form
_____

Expanded Form
_____

Word Form
_____

Complete the chart to show three forms of the number.

	Standard Form	Expanded Form	Word Form
3.		10,000 + 7,000 + 500 + 2	_____ thousand, _____ hundred two
✓ **4.**			eight hundred one thousand, ninety
5.	4,123		_____ thousand, one hundred _____

Name _____

On Your Own

Use the model to write the number three ways.

6.

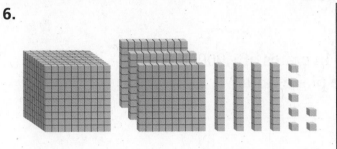

Standard Form

_____

Expanded Form

_____

Word Form

_____

Complete the chart to show three forms of the number.

	Standard Form	Expanded Form	Word Form
7.	1,375		one thousand, _____ hundred _____
8.		600,000 + 9,000 + 10 + 4	six hundred nine thousand, fourteen
9.			eighty-seven thousand, three hundred one

Complete the expanded form.

10. $1,000 +$ _____ $+ 80 + 4 = 1,784$

11. _____ $+ 4,000 + 600 + 90 + 5 = 24,695$

12. $300,000 +$ _____ $+ 100 +$ _____ $= 308,109$

13. $59,273 =$ _____ $+ 9,000 + 200 +$ _____ $+ 3$

14. $804,521 =$ _____ $+ 4,000 + 500 +$ _____ $+ 1$

15. $4,309 =$ _____ $+$ _____ $+$ _____

GO DEEPER **Write the standard form.**

16. 1 hundred thousand 14 ten thousands 16 thousands, 43 tens 2 ones _____

17. $20 + 70,000 + 600 + 9,000 + 8$ _____

18. 35 ones 15 hundreds _____

Problem Solving · Applications (Real World)

19. Unscramble the place values. Write three forms of the number.

4 tens + 8 thousands + 6 ones + 5 hundreds

_____

20. **WRITE** ▸*Math*   How does packing blocks in crates of 1,000, boxes of 100, stacks of 10, and single blocks use place value?

_____

_____

_____

21. **Sense or Nonsense?** Is 8 thousands + 17 hundreds + 29 tens + 10 ones *equal* or *not equal* to 10 thousands? Explain.

_____

_____

_____

_____

_____

_____

22. **GO DEEPER**   Derek wrote the numbers seventeen thousand, eight hundred nineteen and 65,243 on the board. Which of the numbers has a greater value in the thousands place?

_____

23. **THINK SMARTER**   Which is the expanded form of 38,720?

Ⓐ 30,000 + 70 + 2

Ⓑ 3,000 + 800 + 70 + 20

Ⓒ 30,000 + 700 + 20

Ⓓ 30,000 + 8,000 + 700 + 20

WRITE ▸*Math* · **Show Your Work**

Read and Write Numbers Through Hundred Thousands

Lesson Objective You will read and write 6-digit whole numbers in standard, expanded, and word form.

Use the model to write the number in three ways.

1.

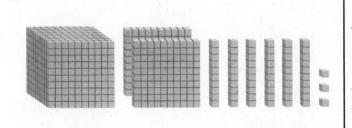

Standard Form
_____ 1,263

Expanded Form
_____

Word Form
_____

Complete the chart to show three forms of the number.

	Standard Form	Expanded Form	Word Form
2.	4,906		_____ thousand, _____ hundred _____
3.		700,000 + 5,000 + 20 + 3	_____ thousand, _____
4.			eighty-one thousand, nine hundred forty-five

Complete the expanded form.

5. _____ + 90,000 + _____ + 10 + 6 = 492,016

Problem Solving Real World

6. The population of a town is 83,393 people. Write the number in expanded form.

7. The number of tourists who visited a national park in one day was nine thousand, twelve. Write this number in two other ways.

_____   _____

Lesson Check

1. Which shows twenty-three thousand, sixteen written in expanded form?

   (A) $2,000 + 300 + 10 + 6$

   (B) $20,000 + 100 + 6$

   (C) $20,000 + 3,000 + 10 + 6$

   (D) $20,000 + 3,000 + 6$

2. Which shows $100,000 + 40,000 + 8,000 + 200 + 80 + 9$ written in standard form?

   (A) 148,089

   (B) 148,280

   (C) 148,289

   (D) 149,089

Spiral Review

3. Which is a way to show the number 5,082?

   (A) 5,082 hundreds

   (B) 50 hundreds 82 ones

   (C) 5 thousands 82 tens

   (D) 5,082 tens

4. Ava writes an even number between 24 and 34. The sum of the digits is odd. Which number could Ava have written?

   (A) 26   (C) 32

   (B) 27   (D) 41

5. How many hundreds are in 47,000?

6. Juanita drew a quick picture to show 31 hundreds. How many tens and ones can she add to her drawing to show 3,147?

_____

_____

Round to the Nearest Ten, Hundred, or Thousand

Learning Objective You will round whole numbers to the nearest ten, hundred, or thousand.

Essential Question How can you round whole numbers to the nearest ten, hundred, or thousand?

CONNECT You have learned to use a number line and place value to round 3-digit numbers to the nearest ten and hundred.

🔑 Unlock the Problem (Real World)

There are 1,459 jelly beans in a jar. What is the number of jelly beans rounded to the nearest thousand?

🔓 One Way Use a number line.

Round 1,459 to the nearest thousand.

To round a number to the nearest thousand, find the thousands it is between.

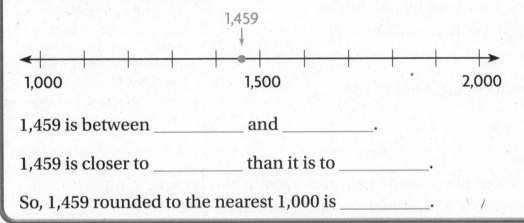

1,459 is between _____ and _____.

1,459 is closer to _____ than it is to _____.

So, 1,459 rounded to the nearest 1,000 is _____.

Try This! **Round 1,459 to the nearest hundred and ten.**

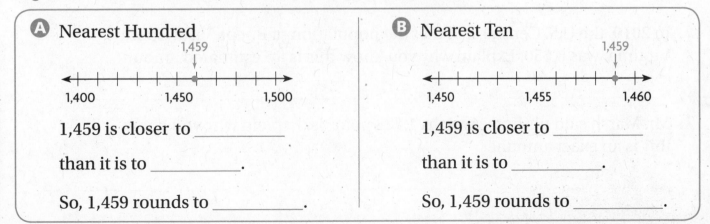

Ⓐ **Nearest Hundred**

1,459 is closer to _____

than it is to _____.

So, 1,459 rounds to _____.

Ⓑ **Nearest Ten**

1,459 is closer to _____

than it is to _____.

So, 1,459 rounds to _____.

🔓 Another Way Use place value.

Round 4,186 to the nearest thousand.

Think: The digit in the hundreds place tells if the number is closer to 4,000 or 5,000.

$$1 \bigcirc 5$$

So, the thousands digit stays the same. Write 4 as the thousands digit. Write zeros for the hundreds, tens, and ones digits.

So, 4,186 rounded to the nearest thousand is _____.

> • Find the place to which you want to round.
> • Look at the digit to the right.
> • If the digit is less than 5, the digit in the rounding place stays the same.
> • If the digit is 5 or greater, the digit in the rounding place increases by one.
> • Write zeros for the digits to the right of the rounding place.

Try This! **Round 4,186 to the nearest hundred.**

Think: The digit in the tens place tells if the number is closer to 4,100 or 4,200.

$$8 \bigcirc 5$$

So, the hundreds digit increases by one. Write 2 as the hundreds digit. Write zeros for the tens and ones digits.

So, 4,186 rounded to the nearest hundred

is _____.

Math Talk

Math Processes and Practices ②

Use Reasoning Which digit do you use to round 4,186 to the nearest ten? Does the digit in the tens place increase by one or stay the same?

An **estimate** tells you about how many or about how much. It is close to an exact amount. Exact amounts represent amounts that can be counted or measured. An estimate represents an amount that is rounded, or that cannot be counted or measured.

1. In 2010, the U.S. Census said that the population of Buena Vista County, Virginia, was 6,650. Explain why you know this is an estimated amount.

_____

2. Mr. Marsh said his horse weighs 1,123 pounds. Explain why you know this is an exact amount.

_____

Name _____

1. Between which two thousands is 7,814? To which thousand is it closer? Round 7,814 to the nearest thousand.

6,000   7,000   8,000   9,000

_____

Round to the nearest thousand, to the nearest hundred, and to the nearest ten.

2. 4,103   ✓ 3. 6,957   4. 4,816   5. 5,379   ✓ 6. 7,493

_____   _____   _____   _____   _____

_____   _____   _____   _____   _____

_____   _____   _____   _____   _____

On Your Own

Math Talk

Math Processes and Practices ②

Use Reasoning What is the greatest number that rounds to 1,000 when rounded to the nearest thousand? Explain.

Round to the nearest thousand, to the nearest hundred, and to the nearest ten.

7. 8,249   8. 4,375   9. 9,502   10. 6,098   11. 2,813

_____   _____   _____   _____   _____

_____   _____   _____   _____   _____

_____   _____   _____   _____   _____

Use the table for 12–13.

12. To the nearest thousand, how many people played musical chairs?

_____

13. To the nearest thousand, the nearest hundred, and the nearest ten, how many people had a snowball fight?

_____

Guinness World Records	
Most people...	Number of People
having a snowball fight	5,387
taking scuba diving lesson	2,465
playing musical chairs	8,238

Problem Solving · Applications (Real World)

Use the table for 14–15.

14. GO DEEPER Round the weights of the giraffe and rhinoceros to the nearest thousand pounds. About how many giraffes would it take to equal the weight of the rhinoceros?

_____

_____

Heaviest Land Mammals	
Animal	**Weight in Pounds**
African Elephant	11,023
Indian Rhinoceros	8,818
Hippopotamus	4,409
Giraffe	2,646

15. **Explain** how to round the weight of the hippopotamus to the nearest thousand, hundred, and ten. _____

_____

_____

_____

16. Asian elephants weigh less than African elephants. One Asian elephant weighed 7,586 pounds. What is 7,586 pounds rounded to the nearest thousand pounds?

_____

17. When rounding to the nearest thousand, what is the greatest number that rounds to 4,000? What is the least number?

_____

18. THINK SMARTER Select the numbers that round to 6,000. Select all that apply.

   (A) 5,480   (C) 6,423

   (B) 5,712   (D) 6,500

Round to the Nearest Ten, Hundred, or Thousand

Round to the nearest thousand, to the nearest hundred, and to the nearest ten.

1. 2,671

2,700;

3,000;

2,670

2. 9,439

_____

_____

_____

3. 3,726

_____

_____

_____

4. 5,604

_____

_____

_____

5. 7,810

_____

_____

_____

6. 8,009

_____

_____

_____

7. 4,547

_____

_____

_____

8. 7,856

_____

_____

_____

9. 6,196

_____

_____

_____

10. 1,958

_____

_____

_____

Problem Solving · Real World

11. There are 7,643 books in the school library. What is the number of books rounded to the nearest thousand, hundred, and ten?

_____

12. There are 5,634 people living in Cara's city. What is 5,634 rounded to the nearest thousand?

_____

13. ‖WRITE ▸*Math* How does the digit in the hundreds place help you round a number to the nearest thousand?

_____

_____

_____

_____

Lesson Check

1. What is 2,641 rounded to the nearest thousand?

   (A) 3,000

   (B) 2,640

   (C) 2,600

   (D) 2,000

2. The digit in which place helps you round a number to the nearest thousand?

   (A) ones

   (B) tens

   (C) hundreds

   (D) thousands

Spiral Review

3. What is fifty-four thousand, seven hundred two written in standard form?

   _____

4. What is the value of the digit 6 in the number 267,913?

   _____

5. Paul's bakery sold 785 donuts. What is 785 rounded to the nearest hundred?

   _____

6. What number is equal to 4 tens 28 ones?

   _____

Name _____

Compare and Order Numbers to Ten Thousand

Learning Objective You will compare and order numbers to 10,000.

Essential Question What are some ways you can compare and order numbers to 10,000?

▲ Top: The Kansas State Capitol
Bottom: The Pennsylvania State Capitol

🔑 Unlock the Problem (Real World)

The Kansas State Capitol is 326 feet tall. The Pennsylvania State Capitol is 272 feet tall. Which building is taller?

You can use symbols to compare numbers.

>   <   =   ≠

greater than   **less than**   **equal to**   **not equal to**

🔒 One Way   Use base-ten blocks.

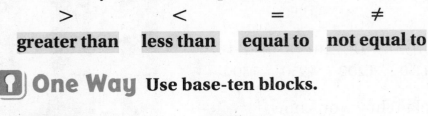
326   272

3 hundreds is _____ than 2 hundreds.

326 ◯ 272   Read: three hundred twenty-six is greater than two hundred seventy-two.

So, the Kansas State Capitol is taller.

Remember

When the number of digits is the same, compare the digits with the greatest place value first.

🔒 Other Ways

A   **Use a number line.**

The numbers on the number line are in order from least to greatest.

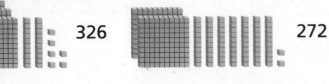
272   326

270   280   290   300   310   320   330

326 is to the right of 272.

So, 326 ◯ 272.

Math Talk   Math Processes and Practices ③

Apply Explain how you know that 78 is less than 312.

B   **Use place value.**

Compare digits in the same place-value position from left to right.

Hundreds	Tens	Ones
3	2	6
2	7	2

3 hundreds is _____ than 2 hundreds.

So, 326 ◯ 272.

Ordering Numbers When you write numbers in order, you write them from greatest to least or least to greatest.

The table shows the names of the tallest buildings in three states. Which building is the tallest?

To find the tallest building, look for the building with the greatest height.

Tallest Buildings in Three States		
State	Building	Height (in feet)
Pennsylvania	Comcast Center	975
New York	Empire State Building	1,250
Georgia	Bank of America Plaza	1,023

One Way Use a number line.

975   1,023   1,250

950 1,000 1,050 1,100 1,150 1,200 1,250 1,300

Which number is greatest? Explain how you know.

_____

Which building is the tallest?

_____

Another Way Use place value.

Order 975; 1,250; and 1,023 from greatest to least.

STEP 1	STEP 2	STEP 3
975	975	975
1,250	1,250	1,250
1,023	1,023	1,023
Compare the number of digits. 975 is the only 3-digit number.	Compare the thousands. They are the same.	Compare the hundreds. 2 is greater than 0.
So, _____ is the least number.	So, look at the hundreds.	So, _____ is greater than _____.

So, the order from greatest to least is _____; _____; _____.

Name _____

Compare the numbers. Write <, >, or = in the ○.

Math Talk Math Processes and Practices ③

Make Arguments When you compare numbers with the same number of digits, why do you compare the digits with greatest value first? Explain.

1. 321 ○ 420

2. 1,604 ○ 864

✓ **3.** 3,751 ○ 3,766

4. 9,007 ○ 9,007

Write the numbers in order from greatest to least.

5. 685, 402, 500

✓ **6.** 2,597; 4,698; 4,689; 3,851

_____, _____, _____

_____; _____; _____; _____

Compare the numbers. Write = or ≠ in the ○.

7. 6,247 ○ 9,247

8. 2,331 ○ 2,331

9. 4,708 ○ 4,807

Compare the numbers. Write <, >, or = in the ○.

10. 850 ○ 731

11. 635 ○ 678

12. 789 ○ 7,890

13. 891 ○ 5,902

14. 5,812 ○ 5,712

15. 8,001 ○ 1,008

16. 6,004 ○ 4,006

17. 4,672 ○ 4,618

18. 4,712 ○ 4,721

19. 3,819 ○ 3,918

20. 6,694 ○ 6,494

21. 8,028 ○ 8,280

Write the numbers in order from least to greatest.

22. 3,628; 3,268; 6,328; 3,826

23. 1,293; 2,032; 1,239; 1,382

_____, _____, _____, _____

_____, _____, _____, _____

Compare the numbers. Write = or ≠ in the ○.

24. 2,201 ○ 2,210

25. 4,321 ○ 4,231

26. 6,749 ○ 6,749

Problem Solving · Applications (Real World)

Marine biologists study plants and animals that live in the ocean. They may count, measure, and weigh the animals.

Use the table for 27–30.

27. Which animal weighs more: the manatee or the bluefin tuna? Explain.

_____

_____

Giants of the Sea (Possible weights and lengths)		
Name	Length (in feet)	Weight (in pounds)
Manatee	12	1,251
Great White Shark	20	4,938
Bluefin Tuna	14	1,759
Giant Clam	39	499

28. Order the weights of the manatee, the great white shark, and the bluefin tuna from least to greatest.

_____

29. Write a number that makes the sentence true.

_____ < 1,251

30. **WRITE** ▸ *Math* **Pose a Problem** Write and solve a comparison problem and use the ≠ symbol.

_____

_____

31. **THINK SMARTER** An elephant at a zoo weighs 4,183 pounds. A rhinoceros at the zoo weighs 4,183 pounds. Which sentence correctly compares the numbers?

Ⓐ 4,183 < 4,183   Ⓒ 4,183 = 4,183

Ⓑ 4,183 > 4,183   Ⓓ 4,183 ≠ 4,183

Name _____

Compare and Order Numbers to Ten Thousand

Learning Objective You will compare and order numbers to 10,000.

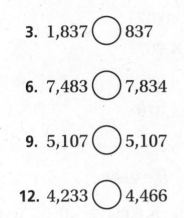

Compare the numbers. Write <, >, or = in the ◯.

1. 835 ◯< 853

2. 5,154 ◯ 5,154

3. 1,837 ◯ 837

4. 560 ◯ 56

5. 2,517 ◯ 2,715

6. 7,483 ◯ 7,834

7. 219 ◯ 2,119

8. 809 ◯ 890

9. 5,107 ◯ 5,107

10. 3,640 ◯ 3,640

11. 9,400 ◯ 10,000

12. 4,233 ◯ 4,466

Write the numbers in order from least to greatest.

13. 246, 235, 241

_____, _____, _____

14. 5,670; 5,760; 5,607; 5,706

_____, _____, _____, _____

Problem Solving Real World

15. The CN Tower in Canada is 1,815 feet tall. The KFVS TV Tower in the United States is 1,677 feet tall. Which tower is taller?

_____

16. There are 2,951 people living in Pearl River and 2,541 people living in Greenville. Which town has fewer people living in it?

_____

17. **WRITE** ▸Math Compare 3,480 and 3,701. Write a sentence using <, >, or =. Explain the method you used.

_____

_____

_____

Lesson Check

1. Which number is less than 4,078?

   (A) 4,807
   (B) 4,707
   (C) 4,087
   (D) 4,076

2. Which shows the numbers in order from least to greatest?

   (A) 1,487; 1,299; 1,499; 1,294
   (B) 1,294; 1,299; 1,487; 1,499
   (C) 1,499; 1,487; 1,299; 1,294
   (D) 1,294; 1,299; 1,499; 1,487

Spiral Review

3. What is $6,000 + 40 + 7$ written in standard form?

4. Daniel thinks of an odd number between 13 and 28. The difference between the digits is 6. What is the number?

5. What is the value of the underlined digit?

   8<u>4</u>,632

6. The digit in which place helps you round a number to the nearest thousand?

Name _____

Add and Subtract Greater Numbers

Essential Question What strategies can you use to add and subtract 4-digit numbers?

Learning Objective You will find sums and differences of 4-digit numbers.

⚷ Unlock the Problem (Real World)

In spring, some monarch butterflies fly 1,867 miles from their winter home in Mexico to South Dakota. They fly another 1,245 miles to reach their summer home in Ontario, Canada. How far do the butterflies fly in all?

🔑 **Use place value to find 1,867 + 1,245.**

THINK	RECORD

Estimate: 1,900 + 1,200 = _____

STEP 1 Add the ones.
Regroup.

12 ones = 1 ten ____ ones

$$\begin{array}{r} \overset{1}{1,86}7 \\ +1,245 \\ \hline \end{array}$$

STEP 2 Add the tens.
Regroup.

11 tens = 1 hundred ____ ten

$$\begin{array}{r} \overset{1\,1}{1,86}7 \\ +1,245 \\ \hline 2 \end{array}$$

STEP 3 Add the hundreds.
Regroup.

11 hundreds = 1 thousand ____ ten

$$\begin{array}{r} \overset{1\,1\,1}{1,86}7 \\ +1,245 \\ \hline 1\,2 \end{array}$$

STEP 4 Add the thousands.

$$\begin{array}{r} \overset{1\,1\,1}{1,86}7 \\ +1,245 \\ \hline ,112 \end{array}$$

So, the butterflies fly _____ miles in all.

Since 3,112 is close to the estimate

of _____, the answer is reasonable.

Math Talk

Math Processes and Practices ①

Make Sense of Problems What is another strategy you could use to solve the problem?

Pelicans Stadium has 2,377 seats. For Saturday's game, 1,849 seats have been sold. How many tickets are left?

🔓 Example   Use place value to find 2,377 − 1,849.

Estimate: 2,400 − 1,800 = _____

STEP 1   Subtract the ones. Since 9 > 7, regroup the tens.
7 tens 7 ones = 6 tens 17 ones

_____ ones − _____ ones = _____ ones

$$\begin{array}{r} \overset{6\ 17}{2,3\cancel{7}\cancel{7}} \\ -1,849 \\ \hline \end{array}$$

STEP 2   Subtract the tens.

_____ tens − _____ tens = _____ tens

$$\begin{array}{r} \overset{6\ 17}{2,3\cancel{7}\cancel{7}} \\ -1,849 \\ \hline 8 \end{array}$$

STEP 3   Subtract the hundreds. Since 8 > 3, regroup the thousands.
2 thousands 3 hundreds = 1 thousand 13 hundreds

_____ hundreds − _____ hundreds = _____ hundreds

$$\begin{array}{r} \overset{1\ 13\ 6\ 17}{\cancel{2},\cancel{3}\cancel{7}\cancel{7}} \\ -1,849 \\ \hline 28 \end{array}$$

STEP 4   Subtract the thousands.

_____ thousand − _____ thousand = _____ thousands

$$\begin{array}{r} \overset{1\ 13\ 6\ 17}{\cancel{2},377} \\ -1,849 \\ \hline 528 \end{array}$$

_____ is close to the estimate of _____, so the answer is reasonable.

So, there are _____ tickets left.

Try This!   Estimate. Then find the sum or difference.

Ⓐ Estimate: _____

$$\begin{array}{r} 7,253 \\ -4,861 \\ \hline \end{array}$$

Ⓑ Estimate: _____

$$\begin{array}{r} 2,498 \\ +3,267 \\ \hline \end{array}$$

Ⓒ Estimate: _____

$$\begin{array}{r} 8,004 \\ -3,526 \\ \hline \end{array}$$

- How can you use addition to check subtraction?

_____

_____

Name _____

Math Talk — Math Processes and Practices 6

Explain a Method
Explain how you regrouped in Exercise 2.

1. Estimate. Then use place value to find 8,203 − 4,251.
   Add to check your answer.

   Estimate: _____ − _____ = _____

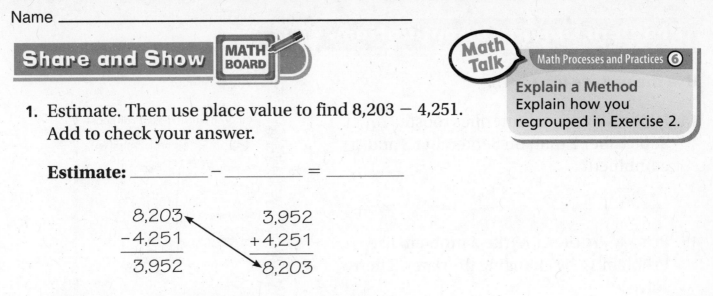

$$
\begin{array}{r} 8,203 \\ -4,251 \\ \hline 3,952 \end{array}
\qquad
\begin{array}{r} 3,952 \\ +4,251 \\ \hline 8,203 \end{array}
$$

Since _____ is close to the estimate of _____,
the answer is reasonable.

Estimate. Then find the sum or difference.

2. Estimate: _____	3. Estimate: _____	4. Estimate: _____	5. Estimate: _____
$\begin{array}{r} 1,805 \\ +4,607 \\ \hline \end{array}$	$\begin{array}{r} 8,319 \\ -3,276 \\ \hline \end{array}$	$\begin{array}{r} 5,041 \\ +\ \ 283 \\ \hline \end{array}$	$\begin{array}{r} 9,621 \\ -7,557 \\ \hline \end{array}$

On Your Own

Estimate. Then find the sum or difference.

6. Estimate: _____	7. Estimate: _____	8. Estimate: _____	9. Estimate: _____
$\begin{array}{r} 3,026 \\ +\ \ 474 \\ \hline \end{array}$	$\begin{array}{r} 4,502 \\ -\ \ 251 \\ \hline \end{array}$	$\begin{array}{r} 2,575 \\ +3,850 \\ \hline \end{array}$	$\begin{array}{r} 8,004 \\ -7,952 \\ \hline \end{array}$

10. Estimate: _____	11. Estimate: _____	12. Estimate: _____	13. Estimate: _____
$\begin{array}{r} 8,319 \\ -3,276 \\ \hline \end{array}$	$\begin{array}{r} 8,719 \\ +1,246 \\ \hline \end{array}$	$\begin{array}{r} 3,308 \\ +5,648 \\ \hline \end{array}$	$\begin{array}{r} 9,621 \\ -7,557 \\ \hline \end{array}$

Problem Solving • Applications (Real World)

Use the picture for 14–15.

14. How many more butterflies roosted on September 2 than on September 3 and 4 combined?

_____

15. Pose a Problem Write a problem like Problem 14 by changing the dates. Then solve.

_____

_____

_____

Monarch Butterflies at Fall Roost	
Date	Number of Butterflies
September 1	923
September 2	2,418
September 3	279
September 4	356

Traveling monarchs rest in large groups called roosts.

16. Josh has put 1,372 pieces of his puzzle together. He has 1,128 pieces left to finish the puzzle. How many pieces are in the puzzle?

_____

17. What's the Error? Mariel found the difference of two 4-digit numbers. Is her answer correct? Explain.

$$\begin{array}{r} \overset{3\ \ 10}{9,4\cancel{0}0} \\ -\ 4,217 \\ \hline 5,193 \end{array}$$

_____

_____

_____

18. **THINK SMARTER** Mark is going to use place value to find the sum of 3,417 + 2,936. In which places will he regroup to add? Mark all that apply.

(A) ones   (C) hundreds

(B) tens   (D) thousands

Add and Subtract Greater Numbers

Learning Objective You will find sums and differences of 4-digit numbers.

Estimate. Then find the sum or difference.

1. Estimate: 6,100 7,345 − 1,213 ‾‾‾‾‾ 6,132	**2.** Estimate: _____ 2,375 + 1,098
3. Estimate: _____ 6,045 + 1,742	**4.** Estimate: _____ 8,300 − 953

5. Estimate: _____ 7,962 − 2,358	**6.** Estimate: _____ 3,658 − 2,491
7. Estimate: _____ 3,407 + 5,936	**8.** Estimate: _____ 6,532 − 1,098

Problem Solving Real World

9. Brad's family traveled 2,645 miles from Los Angeles, California, to Portland, Maine. Then they traveled 1,378 miles from Portland to Biloxi, Mississippi. How many miles did they travel in all?

_____

10. How many fewer miles is it from Portland to Biloxi than it is from Los Angeles to Portland?

_____

11. **WRITE** ▸*Math* Write two different 4-digit numbers. Then describe how to estimate and find the sum or difference of the numbers.

_____

_____

_____

_____

_____

Lesson Check

1. A male rhinoceros in a zoo weighs 7,153 pounds. A female rhinoceros weighs 5,547 pounds. Estimate and then find the difference between the male weight and the female weight.

_____

_____

2. Delia said 2,643 people visited the rhinoceros exhibit at the zoo last weekend. This weekend 1,985 people visited the exhibit. Estimate and then find the total number of visitors.

_____

_____

Spiral Review

3. How can you write seven hundred twenty-six thousand, four hundred three in standard form?

_____

4. An employee at a block factory packed blocks in 4 crates of 1,000, 6 boxes of 100, and 12 single blocks. How many blocks did the employee pack?

_____

5. The number of people who live in Tamara's city is 8,951. Round 8,951 to the nearest ten, the nearest hundred, and the nearest thousand.

_____

6. There are 384 students in third grade classes in Mark's school. There are 348 students in fourth grade classes. Use $<$, $>$, or $=$ to compare the number of students in each grade level.

_____

Name _____

Find an Estimate or Exact Answer

Essential Question How do you know whether an estimate or an exact answer is needed to solve a problem?

Learning Objective You will learn when an estimate or exact answer is needed to solve a problem.

🔑 Unlock the Problem (Real World)

A Boeing 767 airplane that can carry 328 passengers flies from Dallas, Texas, to St. Louis, Missouri, several times each day. The 551-mile trip takes 93 minutes.

• Underline facts you may need to use to solve problems.

Sometimes, you need an exact answer to solve a problem. Sometimes, an estimate is all you need.

🔓 Examples

A Can the airplane carry 624 passengers in two trips?

Since the question asks if the airplane can carry an exact number of passengers, an exact answer is needed.

$$\begin{array}{r} 328 \\ + 328 \\ \hline \end{array}$$

Since 624 ◯ 656, the airplane can carry 624 passengers in two trips.

B About how many minutes will two trips take?

Since the question asks *about* how many minutes, you can estimate to solve.

$$\begin{array}{r} 93 \\ + 93 \\ \hline \end{array} \rightarrow \begin{array}{r} 90 \\ + 90 \\ \hline \end{array}$$

So, two trips will take about _____ minutes, or 3 hours.

Try This! **Tell whether you need an exact answer or an estimate. Then solve.**

A A Boeing 757 has 276 seats. A Boeing 767 has 347 seats. What is the greatest number of passengers the two airplanes can carry together?

_____

B Emma and her family flew on a Boeing 777 last week. They flew 3,627 miles to Paris, France, from New York City, New York. About how many miles is a round trip?

_____

1. The Galleria is the largest mall in Texas. It has 375 stores. The nation's largest mall is the Mall of America in Minnesota. It has 520 stores. About how many more stores does the Mall of America have than The Galleria?

   _____

   Did you need an estimate or an exact answer?
   Think: is the problem asking for about how many or an exact answer?

   _____

✓ 2. How many stores are in both The Galleria and The Mall of America?

   _____

✓ 3. What if the Mall of America had 568 stores? About how many more stores would the Mall of America have than The Galleria?

   _____

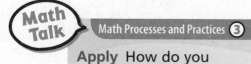

Math Talk

Math Processes and Practices ③

Apply How do you know Problem 3 is asking for an estimate?

On Your Own

Tell whether you need an exact answer or an estimate. Then solve.

4. Alicia wrote a 2-page story for a magazine. Her story must be 1,250 words or fewer. Alicia's first page has 572 words. How many words can her second page have?

   _____

5. The Green Jungle nursery has 782 palm trees. Palm Gardens nursery has 319 palm trees. About how many fewer palm trees does Palm Gardens have than Green Jungle?

   _____

Problem Solving • Applications

Use the table for 6–8. Solve, then tell if you found an estimate or exact answer.

6. How much higher is Waihilau Falls than Yosemite Falls?

_____

Waterfalls Heights (in feet)		
Name	**Location**	**Height**
Angel Falls	Venezuela	3,213
Chamberlain Falls	New Zealand	2,297
Waihilau Falls	Hawaii, U.S.	2,598
Yosemite Falls	California, U.S.	2,425

7. The heights of the two waterfalls in the U.S. are about how much higher than the waterfalls in Venezuela?

_____

WRITE ▸ *Math* · **Show Your Work**

8. **THINK SMARTER** **Pose a Problem** Write a problem like Problem 6 and change the waterfalls.

_____

_____

9. The auditorium has 365 seats. There are 184 fourth-grade students and 178 fifth-grade students. If all the fifth-grade students sit in the auditorium, how many seats are left for fourth-grade students? Did you find an exact answer or an estimate?

_____

10. To be an airline pilot, you must fly a total of at least 1,500 hours. Dan flew 827 hours last year and 582 hours this year. About how many more hours must he fly to be an airline pilot? Do you need an exact answer or an estimate? **Explain.**

_____

_____

11. **THINK SMARTER** **Pose a Problem** Monticello in Charlottesville, Virginia, was the primary plantation of Thomas Jefferson. Daily tours of Monticello are offered year-round. Use the data in the table to write and solve one problem that requires an exact answer and one problem that requires an estimate.

Monticello House Tour	
Day	Number of Visitors
Monday	948
Tuesday	1,023
Wednesday	1,167
Thursday	1,294
Friday	1,580
Saturday	2,365
Sunday	1,791

Exact Answer Problem

Estimate Problem

12. **THINK SMARTER** The school hallway is 225 feet long. If Meredith walks the length of the school hallway 3 times, how far will she have walked? Tell if you solved the problem with an estimate or an exact answer. Show your work.

Find an Estimate or Exact Answer

Learning Objective You will learn when an estimate or exact answer is needed to solve a problem.

Tell whether you need an exact answer or an estimate. Then solve.

Use the data in the table for 1–2.

1. The weight of two polar bears is how much greater than the weight of a giraffe? Do you need an exact answer or an estimate?

   exact answer; 920 pounds
   _____

2. About how much more does a hippopotamus weigh than a water buffalo?

   _____

Weight of Animals	
Animal	**Weight (in Pounds)**
Giraffe	3,500
Hippopotamus	9,900
Polar Bear	2,210
Water Buffalo	2,600

Problem Solving Real World

3. A giraffe at the zoo is 218 inches tall. An ostrich at the zoo is 108 inches tall. About how many inches taller is the giraffe than the ostrich? Did you find an exact answer or an estimate?

   _____

4. On Friday, 1,689 adults and 2,784 children visited the Giant Panda exhibit at the zoo. How many fewer adults visited the zoo than children? Did you find an exact answer or an estimate?

   _____

5. **WRITE** ▸Math Write a problem that can be solved with an exact answer and one that can be solved with an estimate.

   _____

   _____

   _____

   _____

Lesson Check

1. Maria flies 393 miles from her home in Boston, Massachusetts, to Washington, D.C. Then she flies 712 miles from Washington, D.C., to St. Louis, Missouri. How many miles does she fly in all? Did you find an exact answer or an estimate?

_____

_____

2. On Maria's return trip to Boston, she flies 559 miles from St. Louis to Pittsburgh, Pennsylvania. Then she flies 483 miles from Pittsburgh to Boston. About how many miles does she fly on her return trip? Did you find an exact answer or an estimate?

_____

_____

Spiral Review

3. A farmer planted 1,754 bean seeds and 2,689 lettuce seeds. How many bean and lettuce seeds did he plant?

_____

4. The Utah State Capitol is 286 feet tall. The Kansas State Capitol is 326 feet tall. The Iowa State Capitol is 275 feet tall. Write the heights of the capitol buildings in order from greatest to least.

_____

5. Frank has collected 2,064 military buttons, and Mark has collected 3,259 military buttons. Compare the value of the digit 2 in 2,064 to the value of the digit 2 in 3,259.

_____

_____

6. The length of the Rio Grande river in Texas is 1,759 feet. Round the length of the Rio Grande to the nearest thousand, hundred, and ten.

_____

_____

Name _____

Collect Data

Essential Question What are some ways you can collect and organize data?

Learning Objective You will interpret data collected through surveys, observations, and experiments.

Unlock the Problem (Real World)

Conducting a **survey** is one way to collect data. When you ask people questions and record their answers, you are conducting a survey. Making an **observation** is another way to collect data. When you collect data by looking at an object or event, you are making an observation. You can also perform experiments to collect data.

Activity Conduct a survey of the students in your class and record the results in a frequency table.

STEP 1 Think of a survey question that has at least three possible answers. Write your question below.

Survey question: _____

_____

STEP 2 Complete the labels of the frequency table. Include a title and headings. List at least three possible answers to your question.

	Number

STEP 3 Take a survey of the students in your class. Record the results in your frequency table.

STEP 4 Analyze your data.

Which choice got the most votes?

_____

Which choice did the least number of people choose?

_____

How many students did you survey? _____

Math Talk

Math Processes and Practices ③

Compare Representations Describe how your survey results compare with those of a friend.

Examples

A You can collect data by observing, or watching things that happen.

Carl studied three manatees during June, July, and August. He recorded how many times he saw each of the manatees each month.

▲ Manatees are large plant-eating mammals that live in warm water.

	Bandit	Midnight	Owen
June	‖‖	‖‖	‖‖‖
July	‖	‖‖‖ ‖	‖‖‖ ‖‖‖
August	‖	‖‖‖‖	‖‖‖ ‖‖‖

1. How many times did Carl see any of the three manatees during June? _____

2. Which manatee did Carl see most often? _____

3. During which month did Carl see the manatees the most? _____

> **Math Talk**
>
> Math Processes and Practices ②
>
> **Use Reasoning** How might the manatee data be used?

B You can collect data from an **experiment**. An experiment is a test you do to find out something.

Toss a coin 25 times to find how many times it shows heads. Record the results in a tally table. Then show the data in the frequency table at the right.

Coin Toss Results	
Heads	
Tails	

4. Explain what the result of the 26th toss might be.

_____

_____

© Houghton Mifflin Harcourt Publishing Company • Image Credits: ©Marty Snyderman/Corbis

Use the frequency table for 1–3.

Favorite Sport	
Sport	Number
Basketball	7
Soccer	9
Baseball	6
Football	4

1. How many more students voted for soccer than for basketball? _____

2. How many students in all voted for football or baseball? _____

3. How many students voted in all? _____

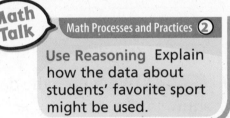

Math Talk Math Processes and Practices ②

Use Reasoning Explain how the data about students' favorite sport might be used.

On Your Own

Use the Shirt Colors list for 4–6.

Shirt Colors	
Jen - white	Kim - blue
Patty - red	Lee - red
Matt - blue	Pam - white
Jared - white	Brad - red
Carl - green	Jake - blue

4. Kelly made a list of the colors of shirts that some of the students in her class were wearing. Use the table to organize her data into a frequency table.

5. How many fewer students were wearing blue or green shirts than white or red shirts? _____

6. GO DEEPER What is another observation Kelly could make about her classmates?

_____

_____

7. WRITE ▸Math Write a survey question about music. Provide at least three possible answer choices to your question.

_____

_____

Problem Solving • Applications (Real World)

Use the Tile Experiment table for 8–10.

Tile Experiment	
Color	Tally
Red	IIII
Blue	IIII IIII IIII II
Green	IIII II

8. Caitlin pulled color tiles from a bag one at a time and then put them back. Which color did she pull most often? How many times?

_____

9. **WRITE** *Math* Write and solve a problem that matches the data in the table.

_____

_____

10. **GO DEEPER** What does the data in the tally table show you?

_____

_____

11. **Sense or Nonsense?** Greg used a tally table to record the number of cards he has in his sports card collection. Then he used a frequency table to show his data. Does Greg's frequency table make sense? **Explain.**

Greg's Sports Cards	
Sport	Tally
Hockey	IIII I
Baseball	IIII IIII III
Football	IIII IIII II
Basketball	IIII IIII

Greg's Sports Cards	
Sport	Number
Hockey	6
Baseball	8
Football	12
Basketball	10

_____

_____

_____

12. **THINK SMARTER** Jen made a tally table to record how many people have dogs as pets. Her table shows

Dog IIII IIII IIII

How many people have dogs as pets?

(A) 4   (B) 9   (C) 14   (D) 15

Collect Data

Learning Objective You will interpret data collected through surveys, observations, and experiments.

Use the Favorite School Subject data for 1–4.

Joe asked his friends about their favorite subject in school.

He made a list of the results of his survey.

Show the data in a tally table and in a frequency table.

Favorite School Subject	
	Ben - Science
Grace - Math	Lauren - Math
Sean - Science	Carlos - Science
Hannah - Science	Mary - Social Studies
Patrick - Social Studies	Jeremy - Reading
Manuel - Math	Matthew - Science

Favorite School Subject	
Subject	**Tally**
Math	|||
Science	
Social Studies	
Reading	

Favorite School Subject	
Subject	**Number**
Math	3
Science	
Social Studies	
Reading	

1. Which subject did the most students choose as their favorite?

_____

2. How many more students chose math than reading?

_____

Problem Solving *Real World*

3. How would the results of Joe's survey change if Jeremy was not asked about his favorite subject?

_____

_____

4. How many more votes would social studies need to have the same number as math?

_____

_____

Lesson Check

Favorite Winter Sport	
Sport	Number
Ice Skating	8
Hockey	4
Sledding	12
Snowboarding	15

1. In the table, *Favorite Winter Sport*, how many people chose snowboarding or hockey as their favorite winter sport?

Ⓐ 8

Ⓑ 12

Ⓒ 16

Ⓓ 19

Spiral Review

2. Austin is going to subtract 3,597 from 5,102. In which places will he regroup to subtract?

3. The observatory had 1,297 visitors on Saturday and 1,185 visitors on Sunday. About how many visitors were at the observatory on the weekend? Did you find an exact answer or an estimate?

4. An airplane flew 1,551 miles from Boston, Massachusetts, to Dallas, Texas. It then flew 2,596 miles from Dallas to Los Angeles, California. How many total miles did the airplane fly?

5. A manatee's weight was recorded as 1,257 pounds. Round 1,257 to the nearest thousand, hundred, and ten pounds.

Name _____

Analyze and Interpret Data

Essential Question How can you draw conclusions and make predictions using different graphs?

Learning Objective You will draw conclusions and make predictions based on data in bar graphs and pictographs.

🔑 Unlock the Problem (Real World)

A **conclusion** is a statement based on given data. To draw a conclusion, you look at the facts and tell what you know based on this information.

Sometimes you can make a prediction based on data. A **prediction** is a reasonable guess about what may happen. Predictions may end up being true or false.

- What facts does the bar graph show?

  _____

  _____

- For how many days did Mr. Richards record the data? _____

🔓 Example 1 Use a bar graph.

Mr. Richards is a park ranger. He recorded the number of hikers who visited the park each day for 5 days.

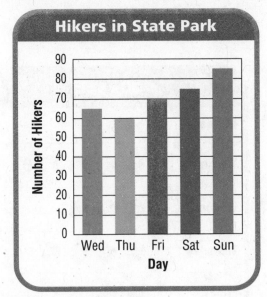

Hikers in State Park

Math Talk

Math Processes and Practices ②

Use Reasoning Explain why the greatest number of people might go to the park on Sunday.

A **Draw a conclusion.**

On which day did the greatest number of hikers visit the park?

Conclusion: The greatest number of

hikers visited on _____.

B **Make a prediction.**

On which day next week will the greatest number of hikers probably visit the park?

Prediction: Next week, the most

hikers will probably visit on _____.

Example 2 Use a pictograph.

Mr. Richards leads five nature walks each day. On Monday, he recorded the number of chipmunks he saw on each walk.

A Draw a conclusion about the number of chipmunks Mr. Richards saw.

Conclusion: The number of chipmunks _____ after noon.

B Make a prediction about the number of chipmunks Mr. Richards will see at 8:00 P.M. Explain.

Prediction: Mr. Richards will see _____ chipmunks at 8:00 P.M.

_____

_____

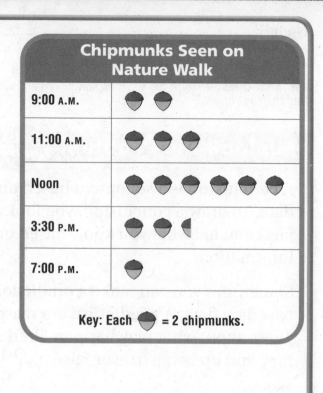

Chipmunks Seen on Nature Walk	
9:00 A.M.	
11:00 A.M.	
Noon	
3:30 P.M.	
7:00 P.M.	

Key: Each = 2 chipmunks.

Share and Show MATH BOARD

Use the pictograph for 1–2.

1. Joanna works at a music store. The pictograph shows the number of CDs sold each day last week. The least number of CDs was sold on Joanna's day off. Draw a conclusion about the day Joanna had off.

   Conclusion: _____

2. Next week, Joanna has to work on the day the store expects to sell the most CDs. Make a prediction about which day Joanna will work next week. Explain why your prediction is reasonable.

   Prediction: _____

   _____

   _____

CDs Sold	
Monday	
Tuesday	
Wednesday	
Thursday	
Friday	

Key: Each = 10 CDs.

Math Talk

Math Processes and Practices ⑥

Compare Explain the difference between a conclusion and a prediction.

Name _____

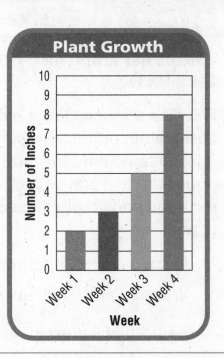

On Your Own

Use the bar graph for 3–5.

3. Courtney made a bar graph to show the number of inches her plant grew each week. Draw a conclusion about the number of inches Courtney's plant grew.

   _____

4. Courtney plans to measure the growth of her plant again at 5 weeks. Make a prediction about the plant's growth.

   _____

5. **WRITE** ▸*Math* When Courtney measured the plant at Week 5, its height was 8 inches. Does this match the prediction you made in Problem 4? Explain.

   _____

Problem Solving • Applications *Real World*

Use the bar graph for 6–7.

6. The marbles in a bag are red, blue, yellow, and green. Grant pulled 55 marbles and recorded the results in the graph. If Grant counted all the marbles in the bag, which color would most likely outnumber the others? Explain.

   _____

   _____

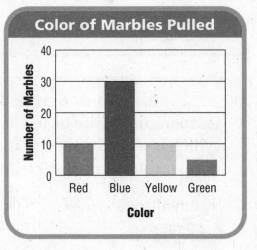

Color of Marbles Pulled

7. **GO DEEPER** Draw a conclusion about the number of red marbles compared to green marbles in the bag.

   _____

   _____

Connect to Science

Use the bar graph for 8–10.
Gray Wolves

Kelly is a scientist. From hidden observation points, she gathered information about the number of pups born to 8 gray wolves. She recorded and graphed the number of pups.

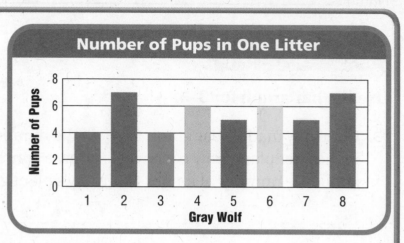

Number of Pups in One Litter

8. Circle a correct interpretation of the bar graph.

Wolves 2 and 8 had the same number of pups in one litter.

Wolf 3 had 3 pups in one litter.

Wolves 5 and 7 had fewer pups in one litter than any of the other wolves.

9. Draw a conclusion about the number of pups born in one litter.

_____

10. **What if** wolves 1 and 3 had each had 2 more pups in their litters? How would your conclusion in Problem 9 change?

_____

11. 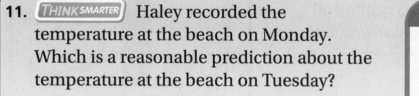 Haley recorded the temperature at the beach on Monday. Which is a reasonable prediction about the temperature at the beach on Tuesday?

   (A) It will be warmer at 10:00 A.M. than at 2:00 P.M.

   (B) It will be coolest at 2:00 P.M.

   (C) It will be warmest at 8:00 A.M.

   (D) It will be colder at 8:00 A.M. than at 10:00 A.M.

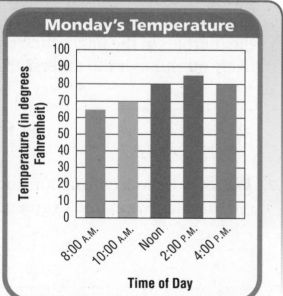

Monday's Temperature

Analyze and Interpret Data

Learning Objective You will draw conclusions and make predictions based on data in bar graphs and pictographs.

Use the bar graph for 1–3.

1. A movie theater is showing four types of movies on Friday and Saturday. Draw a conclusion about the number of people who attended the animated movie on Friday night.

   The least number of people watched the animated

   movie on Friday night.

   _____

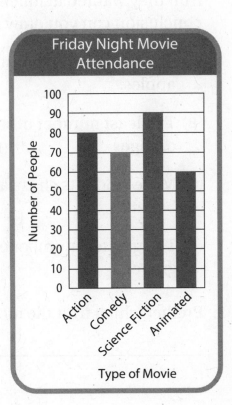

Friday Night Movie Attendance

2. Make a prediction about which type of movie the greatest number of people will attend on Saturday night. Explain.

   _____

   _____

   _____

   _____

Problem Solving · Real World

3. Mr. Reynolds owns the movie theater. He wants to add extra show times for the two most popular types of movies. Draw a conclusion. Which two types of movies should Mr. Reynolds choose? Explain your reasoning.

   _____

   _____

   _____

Lesson Check

Use the pictograph for 1–2.

1. Students were asked to choose which fruit they wanted at lunch one day. Which conclusion can you draw from the graph?

   (A) The least number of students chose apples.

   (B) The least number of students chose oranges.

   (C) More students chose apples than bananas.

   (D) The greatest number of students chose grapes.

Fruit Choices	
Apples	☺ ☺ ☺ ☺
Bananas	☺ ☺ ☺ ☺ ☺ ☺
Oranges	☺
Grapes	☺ ☺ ☺

Key: Each ☺ = 2 students.

2. Predict which fruit the most students will choose the next day.

Spiral Review

3. There are 6 teachers and 105 students at the assembly. How many people are at the assembly?

4. One weekend, 4,537 people visited the Space Exhibit at the science museum. What is 4,537 rounded to the nearest thousand?

5. Chris is making a pictograph to show his classmates' favorite kind of TV show. He plans to use one picture of a TV to represent 5 students. How many TVs will he use to represent 15 people?

6. Nell has 41 postcards. Twenty-two postcards are displayed on her wall. The rest are in her desk. How many postcards are in Nell's desk?

Name _____

Probability: Likelihood of Events

Essential Question How can you describe the probability of an event happening?

Learning Objective You will decide if an event is likely, unlikely, certain, or impossible.

An **event** is something that might happen.
Probability is the chance that an event will happen.

Unlock the Problem Real World

Tyler is going to pull a marble out of this bag without looking. The marbles all have the same shape and size. Is it likely, unlikely, certain, or impossible that Tyler will pull a red marble?

Pulling red is **likely.** It has a good chance of happening.

Pulling yellow is **unlikely.** It does not have a good chance of happening.

In this bag, pulling red is **certain.** It will always happen.

Pulling green is **impossible.** It will never happen.

Tyler's bag has more _____ marbles than blue or yellow marbles.

So, it is _____ that Tyler will pull a red marble.

- Is Tyler more likely to pull a blue marble or a yellow marble? Explain.

_____

_____

_____

_____

Try This! If you spin the pointer one time, write whether the event is *likely*, *unlikely*, *certain*, or *impossible*.

- The pointer will land on green. _____
- The pointer will land on red. _____
- The pointer will land on blue. _____
- The pointer will land on green, blue or yellow. _____

Share and Show

Use the bag of marbles for 1.

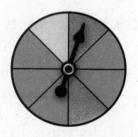

1. The bag contains yellow, blue, and green marbles.

   The most marbles are _____.

   The fewest marbles are _____.

   So, a _____ marble is likely to be pulled.

Use the spinner for 2–5. If you spin the pointer one time, write whether the event is *likely*, *unlikely*, *certain*, or *impossible*.

2. The pointer will land on red.

   _____

⊘ 3. The pointer will land on yellow.

   _____

⊘ 4. The pointer will land on green.

   _____

5. The pointer will land on red, yellow, or blue.

   _____

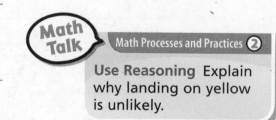

Math Talk Math Processes and Practices ②

Use Reasoning Explain why landing on yellow is unlikely.

Name _____

On Your Own

Use the bag of marbles for 6–9. If you pull one marble from the bag without looking, write whether the event is *likely, unlikely, certain,* or *impossible.*

6. pulling a yellow marble _____

7. pulling a red, green, or yellow marble _____

8. pulling a blue marble _____

9. pulling a red marble _____

Use the spinner for 10–13. If you spin the pointer one time, write whether the event is *likely, unlikely, certain,* or *impossible.*

10. The pointer will land on A, B, or C. _____

11. The pointer will land on C. _____

12. The pointer will land on D. _____

13. The pointer will land on A. _____

Use the table for 14–16. Jay pulls one sock from his drawer without looking.

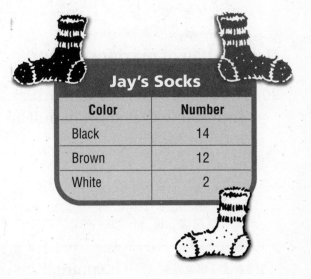

Jay's Socks

Color	Number
Black	14
Brown	12
White	2

14. Is it likely or unlikely that Jay will pull a white sock? _____

15. Is it certain or impossible that Jay will pull a blue sock? _____

16. **WRITE** ▸*Math* What if Jay had 30 more white socks. **Explain** how your answer to Problem 14 would change.

_____

_____

Problem Solving • Applications Real World

Use the bag of tiles for 17–18.

17. Alicia has this bag of number tiles. The tiles are the same size and shape. Is it likely or unlikely that she will pull a 3-tile without looking? Explain.

_____

_____

18. **WRITE** ▸Math Suppose 7 number 3 tiles are added to the bag. **Explain** how your answer to Problem 17 would change.

_____

_____

19. Stefan put 16 red tiles in a box. Of the tiles, 4 had the letter X, 2 had the letter Y, and 10 had the letter Z. The tiles are the same size and shape. Is it certain or likely that Stefan will pull a Z tile without looking? Explain.

_____

Use the bag of marbles for 20.

20. Luvina has this bag of marbles. Is it unlikely or impossible that she will pull an orange marble without looking?

_____

_____

21. **THINK SMARTER** The pointer on this spinner is spun once. On which color is the pointer likely to land?

    (A) yellow   (C) red

    (B) blue   (D) green

Probability: Likelihood of Events

Learning Objective You will decide if an event is likely, unlikely, certain, or impossible.

Use the spinner for 1–3. If you spin the pointer one time, write if the event is *likely, unlikely, certain,* **or** *impossible.*

1. The pointer will land on yellow.

   Think: Only 1 out of 6 equal sections of the spinner is yellow.

   _____ **unlikely** _____

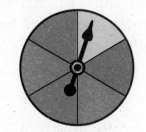

2. The pointer will land on red, yellow, or blue.

   _____

3. The pointer will land on green.

   _____

Problem Solving *Real World*

4. Kyle has a bag with 20 stamps in all. He has 4 flag stamps, 10 car stamps, 2 plane stamps, and 4 eagle stamps. All the stamps are the same size and shape. Kyle picks 1 stamp without looking. Which type of stamp is Kyle unlikely to pick?

   _____

   _____

5. Suppose 10 additional plane stamps are added to Kyle's bag of stamps. Does your answer to Problem 4 change? Explain.

   _____

   _____

   _____

6. Write a question about Kyle's bag of stamps. The answer is flag stamps, car stamps, plane stamps, or eagle stamps.

   _____

   _____

   _____

7. **WRITE** *Math* Describe the chance that an event will happen. Use the words *likely, unlikely, certain,* or *impossible.*

   _____

   _____

Lesson Check

Use the bag of marbles for 1–2.

1. Chelsea is going to pull a marble from this bag without looking. The marbles are the same size and shape. What color marble is Chelsea unlikely to pull?

   _____

2. Is it certain or impossible that Chelsea will pull a blue marble from the bag?

   _____

Spiral Review

3. Lake Tahoe is 501 feet deep. Lake Superior is 406 feet deep. Crater Lake is 594 feet deep. Write the lake depths in order from least to greatest.

   _____

4. What are two other ways you can write the number 307,986?

   _____

5. A block factory packs blocks in crates of 1,000, boxes of 100, stacks of 10, and single blocks. What is one way Julia can pack an order for 2,349 blocks without using crates?

   _____

6. Do you need an exact answer or an estimate to find the difference between the number of adults and children at a softball game?

   _____

Name _____

Possible Outcomes

Essential Question How can you describe possible outcomes?

Unlock the Problem Real World   Hands On

When you toss a coin, there are two possible results. In probability, a possible result is called an **outcome**.

The possible outcomes in a coin toss are *heads* and *tails*. The outcomes *heads* and *tails* are **equally likely** because each has the same chance of happening.

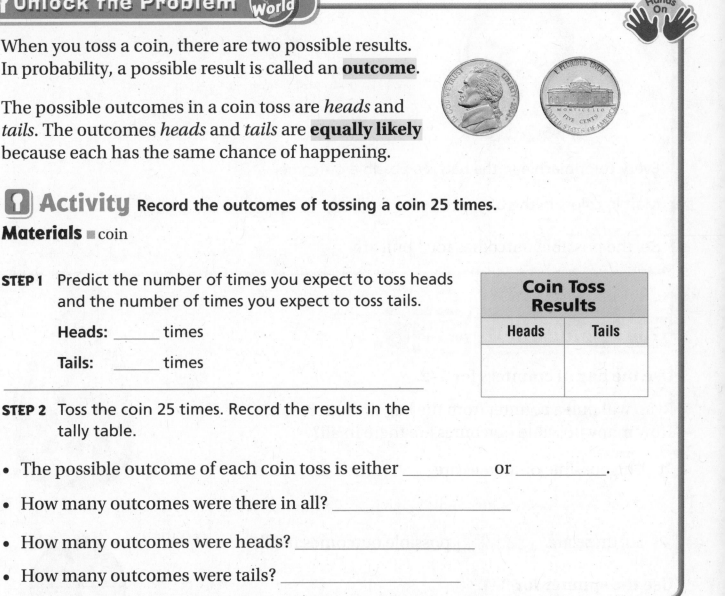

Activity Record the outcomes of tossing a coin 25 times.

Materials ■ coin

STEP 1 Predict the number of times you expect to toss heads and the number of times you expect to toss tails.

Heads: _____ times

Tails: _____ times

Coin Toss Results	
Heads	**Tails**

STEP 2 Toss the coin 25 times. Record the results in the tally table.

- The possible outcome of each coin toss is either _____ or _____.

- How many outcomes were there in all? _____

- How many outcomes were heads? _____

- How many outcomes were tails? _____

1. Was your prediction close to the actual results? Explain.

_____

_____

2. What if you tossed the coin 50 times? Predict how many times you would expect to toss heads.

_____

🔑 Example List all the possible outcomes for the event.

Cal is going to pull one marble from the bag without looking. What are the possible outcomes for 1 pull?

Think: The possible outcomes does not mean the total number of marbles in the bag but the total number of different kinds of marbles.

Every color marble in the bag is a possible outcome.

Marble colors in the bag are: _____ , _____ , _____ .

So, the possible outcomes for 1 pull are _____ , _____ , _____ .

Use the bag of counters for 1–2.

Ryan will pull a counter from the bag without looking. How many possible outcomes are there in all?

1. The possible outcomes are _____ .

   Think: every color counter in the bag is a possible outcome.

2. So, there are _____ possible outcomes in all.

Use the spinner for 3–4.

Karinna spins the pointer. Which outcomes are equally likely?

✓ 3. The possible outcomes are

   _____ .

✓ 4. So, the equally likely outcomes are

   _____ .

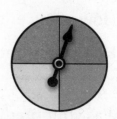

Math Talk   Math Processes and Practices ④

Use Repeated Reasoning Explain why the probabilities of the pointer landing on green, blue, yellow, or red are equally likely.

On Your Own

List all the possible outcomes for the event.

5. Kyle will toss a quarter.

_____

6. McKenna will spin the pointer.

_____

7. Octavio will pull a number tile.

_____

8. Julie will roll a cube that is numbered 1–6.

_____

Describe if the outcomes are *equally likely* or *not equally likely*.

9. Anna will spin the pointer one time.

_____

10 James will pull 1 marble.

_____

Problem Solving • Applications

Use the bag of marbles for 12–13.

12. Felicia is going to pull 1 marble from the bag without looking. What are the possible outcomes for 1 pull?

_____

13. **Sense or Nonsense?** Felicia says that pulling a red marble is as equally likely as pulling a green marble. Does her statement make sense?

_____

_____

_____

14. Alfredo drew a spinner with 8 equal sections. Three sections are yellow. Landing on yellow and landing on blue are equally likely. How many sections are blue? Draw to show what the spinner might look like.

_____

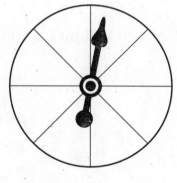

15. Mario is going to pull 1 sports card from a box without looking. The box contains 2 football cards, 3 baseball cards, and 2 basketball cards. How many possible outcomes are there for 1 pull? Which outcomes are equally likely?

_____

16. **THINK SMARTER** Devon is going to pick 1 shape card from a box without looking. All cards are the same size and shape. Which two shapes is Devon equally likely to pick?

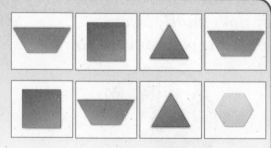

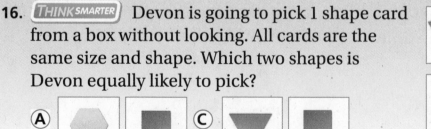

Ⓐ   Ⓒ

Ⓑ   Ⓓ

Possible Outcomes

Learning Objective You will find the possible outcomes for a single event.

List all the possible outcomes for the event.

1. Scott will toss a nickel.

   heads, tails
   _____

2. Joel will spin the pointer one time.

   _____

3. Amelia will roll a cube. that is numbered 1-6.

   _____

Problem Solving Real World

Use the spinner for 4–5.

4. Jordan is going to spin the pointer one time. List all the possible outcomes.

   _____

5. Are the outcomes equally likely or not equally likely?

   _____

6. **WRITE** ▸*Math* Describe a probability experiment that has equally likely outcomes and one that does not have equally likely outcomes.

   _____

   _____

Lesson Check

1. Carly will pull a marble from the bag without looking. What are the possible outcomes for one pull?

   _____

2. Which outcomes are equally likely?

   _____

Spiral Review

3. Lee is going to pull a marble out of this bag without looking. Is it likely, unlikely, certain, or impossible that Lee will pull a green marble?

   _____

4. Felicia collected 430 bottles for recycling. Jorge collected 227 fewer bottles than Felicia. How many bottles did Jorge collect?

   _____

5. A Boeing 777 can carry 396 passengers. A Boeing 767 can carry 375 passengers. How many passengers can the two airplanes carry? Did you find an estimate or exact answer to find the answer?

   _____

6. Casey made a tally table to record his classmates' favorite color. The row for blue shows

   Blue   卌 卌 ||

   How many classmates like blue?

   _____

Number Patterns

Essential Question How can you describe and extend number patterns?

Learning Objective You will describe, extend, and create number patterns.

CONNECT You have learned that a pattern is an ordered set of numbers or objects in which the order helps you predict what will come next. Some patterns are made with numbers that repeat. The part of the pattern that repeats is called a **pattern core**. A **repeating pattern** uses the same pattern core over and over again.

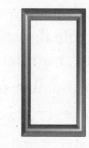

Unlock the Problem · Real World

Mallory makes picture frames. The table shows the number of picture frames she made each week. If the pattern continues, how many picture frames will she make in Week 10?

Week	1	2	3	4	5	6	7	8	9	10
Number of Picture Frames	3	2	4	3	2	4	3	2	4	

Identify a pattern core. Then find the missing number in the pattern.

Look at the pattern in the table. The number pattern is 3, 2, 4, 3, 2, 4, 3, 2, 4.

The pattern core, or the part that repeats, is _____ .

So, Mallory will make _____ picture frames in Week 10.

Try This! Use a pattern core to identify the missing numbers in the pattern.

Find the number of picture frames Mallory will make in Weeks 12 and 17.

Week	10	11	12	13	14	15	16	17	18	19
Number of Picture Frames	3	2		3	2	4	3		4	3

So, Mallory will make _____ picture frames in Week 12

and _____ picture frames in Week 17.

A **growing pattern** increases or decreases the same amount from one number to the next. A **rule** can be used to describe a growing pattern.

🔑 Examples

A Eric wrote a number pattern on the board. What rule describes his pattern? What will the next number be?

Look at the number pattern to find a rule.

Think: What do I do to 4 to get 7? What do I do to 7 to get 10?

4, 7, 10, 13, 16

4   7   10   13   16
+3 +3 +3 +3

The numbers in the pattern grow, or increase by 3.

So, the rule *add* _____ describes his pattern. Use the rule to extend the pattern.

So, the next number will be $16 + 3 =$ _____.

B What rule describes this pattern? What are the missing numbers in the pattern?

Think: What do I do to 29 to get 25? What do I do to 25 to get 21?

29, 25, 21, 17, ■ 9, ■

29 25 21 17 ■ 9 ■
−4 −4 −4 −4 −4 −4

So, the rule *subtract* _____ describes the pattern. Use the rule to find the missing numbers.

So, the missing numbers are $17 - 4 =$ _____ and $9 - 4 =$ _____.

> **Math Idea**
> A rule must be true for all the numbers in the pattern.

C The rule for the pattern is *subtract 6*.

Use the rule to write the numbers in the pattern. Start with 48.

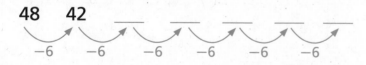

48 42 ____ ____ ____ ____ ____
−6 −6 −6 −6 −6 −6

So, the next five numbers in the pattern are: _____ .

Share and Show

1. 2, 7, 3, 1, 2, 7, 3, 1, 2, 7, 3, 1, 2
   Identify the pattern core. _____
   What are the next two
   numbers in the pattern? _____

2. 28, 38, 48, 58, _____, 78, _____, 98
   What rule describes the pattern?
   _____
   What are the missing numbers in
   the pattern?

Name the pattern core. Then find the missing numbers.

3. 5, 8, 9, 5, 8, 9, 5, 8, _____, 5, 8, 9, _____

   The pattern core is _____.

Write a rule to describe the pattern. Then find the missing numbers.

4. 16, 21, 26, 31, 36, 41, _____, _____

   The rule is _____.

5. 37, _____, 31, 28, 25, _____, 19, 16

   The rule is _____.

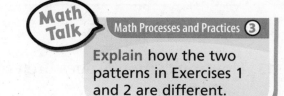

Math Talk — Math Processes and Practices ③

Explain how the two patterns in Exercises 1 and 2 are different.

On Your Own

Name the pattern core. Then find the missing numbers.

6. 56, 35, 19, 7, 56, _____, 19, 7, 56, 35, _____, 7

   The pattern core is _____.

Write a rule to describe the pattern. Then find the missing numbers.

7. 27, _____, 45, 54, 63, _____, 81, 90

   The rule is _____.

Use a pattern core or a rule to write the numbers in the pattern.

8. 42, 40, 44, repeat. 42, 40, 44, _____, _____, _____, _____, _____, _____, _____, _____

9. Subtract 3. Start with 36. 36, _____, _____, _____, _____, _____, _____

10. GO DEEPER Write a rule to describe this pattern 26, 23, 20, 17, 14, 11, 8.
    Then use your rule to make another pattern that has the same rule.

    _____

Problem Solving • Applications

11. **GO DEEPER** **What's the Error?** Bella wrote this pattern: 5, 12, 15, 22, 25, 32, 35. Eduardo said the rule is *add 7*. Describe his error. Write a correct rule.

_____

_____

12. **GO DEEPER** Write a rule to describe this number pattern 3, 9, 15, 21. Then write another number pattern using the same rule. Write the first four numbers in your pattern.

_____

Use the table for 13–15.

13. How much money does Brett save each week?

_____

14. How much money will be in Brett's account in Week 7?

_____

15. Brett wants a bike that costs $76. If he continues the savings pattern, will he have enough saved by Week 10? Explain.

_____

_____

Brett's Savings	
Week	Amount
1	$6
2	$12
3	$18
4	$24
5	$30
6	$36

16. **THINK SMARTER** What are the missing numbers in this pattern?

62, 59, 56, ■, 50, 47, 44, ■, 38

(A) 55 and 43   (C) 53 and 41

(B) 53 and 42   (D) 57 and 45

Algebra • Number Patterns

Learning Objective You will describe, extend, and create number patterns.

Name the pattern core. Then find the missing numbers.

1. 96, 93, ___24___, 96, ___93___, 24, 96, 93, 24, 96

   The pattern core is _____.

2. 5, 13, 21, 29, 5, 13, 21, 29, 5, 13, 21, 29, 5, 13, 21, _____, _____, _____

   The pattern core is _____.

Write a rule to describe the pattern. Then find the missing numbers.

3. 73, 77, _____, 85, 89, _____, 97, 101

   The rule is _____.

4. 64, 58, 52, 46, 40, 34, _____, _____

   The rule is _____.

Use a pattern core or a rule to write the numbers in the pattern.

5. 1, 1, 5, 5, repeat.

   1, 1, _____, 5, 1, _____, 5, 5, _____, 1, 5, 5

6. Add 7. Start with 44.

   44, _____, _____, _____, _____, _____, _____, _____

Problem Solving Real World

7. Juan is using an addition rule to find each number in the pattern below.

   39, ■, 57, 66, 75, 84

   What number is missing in the pattern?

   _____

8. Claire wrote a number pattern. The third number in her pattern is 15. She used the rule *add 5*. What number did Claire choose as the starting number?

   _____

9. **WRITE** ▸*Math* Dylan's pattern is: 38, 35, 32, 29, 26, 23. Explain how to find a rule that describes his pattern. What is the next number?

   _____

   _____

Lesson Check

1. Carli is using the rule *add 4* to find each number in the pattern below.

   31, 35, 39, 43, 47, ■, ■

   What two numbers come next in Carli's pattern?

   _____

2. Trevor wrote the number pattern below.

   12, 17, ■, 12, 17, 22, 12, ■, 22, 12

   Identify the pattern core and find the missing numbers in Trevor's pattern.

   _____

Spiral Review

3. Iris spins the pointer. Which outcomes are equally likely?

   _____

4. If the answer choices in a survey are spring, summer, fall, and winter, what might the survey question be?

   _____

5. Jasper has 1,604 coins in his collection. Nellie has 429 more coins than Jasper. How many coins does Nellie have? Tell whether you need an exact answer or an estimate. Then solve the problem.

   _____

   _____

6. Compare the value of the digit 4 in 400 to the value of the digit 4 in 4,000.

   _____

   _____

Name _____

Patterns in Tables

Essential Question How can you use a rule to extend and find missing numbers in a table?

Learning Objective You will use a rule to extend and find missing numbers in input/output tables.

🔑 Unlock the Problem (Real World)

Noel's school is having a book fair. With any purchase, you can buy a puzzle book for $2. Noel's purchase total was $47 and he wants to buy a puzzle book. How much will he spend?

An **input/output table** matches each input value with an output value. The output depends on the input. A **rule** describes the relationship between the input and the output.

- Underline what you are asked to find.
- Circle what you need to use.

🔒 Use the rule to complete the table.

- Identify a rule.

  Think: The output is $2 _____ than the input.

  The rule is _____ to the input.

- Use the rule to complete the table.

  Think: To find the output, add $2 to the input.

Final cost: $47 + _____ = _____

So, Noel will spend _____ .

Book Fair Sale

Input	Output
$4	$6
$9	
$15	
$28	
$36	
$47	

Math Talk

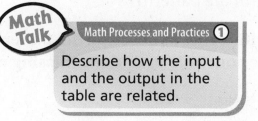

Math Processes and Practices ①

Describe how the input and the output in the table are related.

Try This! Use the rule *subtract 6 from the input* to complete the table.

Input	9	25	34	48	60	73
Output						

🔑 Examples

A Write a rule to describe the pattern in the table. Use your rule to find the missing numbers.

Rule: _____ from the input to get the output.

Input	Output
67	62
58	53
49	
30	25
26	
15	

Think:
67−5 = 62

58−5 = 53

B Use the rule *add 16 to the input* to complete the table.

Input	22	35	44	57	63	76
Output	38			73		

! ERROR Alert

A rule must work for each pair of numbers in the table. Be sure to test your rule with each pair of numbers in the table.

Share and Show

1. Rule: Add 15 to the input. What are the next two numbers in the pattern?

Input	7	12	24	36	45	57
Output	22	27	39	51		

Write a rule to describe the pattern in the table. Use your rule to find the missing numbers.

✓ 2.

Input	22	41	64	73	85	100
Output	14		56			92

Rule: _____

✓ 3.

Input	37	54	69	80	99	118
Output		67		93		131

Rule: _____

Math Talk

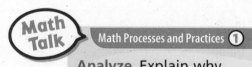

Math Processes and Practices ❶

Analyze Explain why it is important to test your rule with each pair of numbers in an input/output table.

Name _____

Use the rule to complete the table.

4. Add 9 to the input.

Input	12	25	31	43	59	62
Output	21	34	40			

5. Subtract 12 from the input.

Input	74	60	51	47	30	21
Output	62	48	39			

Write a rule to describe the pattern in the table.
Use your rule to find the missing numbers.

6.

Input	Output
37	
42	49
56	
63	
71	78
80	87

7.

Input	Output
142	131
136	125
124	
119	
108	97
97	

Rule: _____

Rule: _____

8.

Input	14	26	37	45		
Output	19	31	42	50	63	68

Rule: _____

9. **GO DEEPER** Write a rule for the table.
Then use your rule to complete the table.

Input	82	74	65	58	49	36
Output						

Problem Solving • Applications (Real World)

Use the table for 10–11.

10. Write a rule to describe the pattern in the table. Use your rule to extend the pattern.

_____

11. **WRITE** ▸*Math* **What's the Question?** Shauna has $12 in her hot lunch account on Friday after buying lunch each school day that week. The answer is $27.

_____

_____

Hot Lunch Accounts	
Before Lunch	**After Lunch**
$16	$13
$24	$21
$29	$26
$33	$30
$38	$35
$41	$38

Use the table for 12.

12. Phillip earns money doing chores. He puts some of the money into a savings account. What rule describes the pattern in the table? If the pattern continues, how much will Phillip save if he earns $53?

_____

_____

_____

Phillip's Chores	
Money Earned	**Money Saved**
$22	$15
$25	$18
$31	$24
$37	$30
$40	$33

13. **THINK SMARTER** Which rule describes the pattern in the table?

Input	17	30	43	56	69
Output	25	38	51	64	77

(A) Add 8 to the input.

(B) Subtract 3 from the input.

(C) Subtract 8 from the input.

(D) Add 13 to the input.

Algebra • Patterns in Tables

Use the rule to complete the table.

1. Subtract 9 from the input.

Input	16	27	35	48	59	72
Output	7	18	26	39		

2. Add 11 to the input.

Input	44	57	65	82	91	114
Output	55			93	102	

**Write a rule to describe the pattern in the table.
Use your rule to find the missing numbers.**

3.

Input	Output
92	87
104	99
123	118
130	
141	

4.

Input	Output
97	109
118	
126	138
144	
160	172

Rule: _____

Rule: _____

Problem Solving Real World

5. A restaurant charges a flat fee for delivery. What rule describes the pattern in the table? Before the delivery fee is added, the cost of Mr. Brewer's order is $36. What is the total amount Mr. Brewer will pay to have is order delivered?

Input	$13	$18	$22	$26	$31	$36
Output	$20	$25	$29	$33		

_____

Lesson Check

Use the table for 1–2.

1. Curtis is drawing rectangles. In the table, the width of the rectangles is the input, and the length is the output. Write a rule to describe the pattern in the table.

Rectangles	
Input	Output
4	8
7	11
12	16
16	20
23	27

_____

2. Curtis draws a rectangle with a width of 29 units. What is the length, in units, of the rectangle?

_____

Spiral Review

3. What is a rule that describes this pattern?

   65, 58, 51, 44, 37, 30, 23, 16

_____

4. What is 45,623 rounded to the nearest ten?

_____

5. If you pull one marble from the bag, what color marble are you likely to pull?

_____

6. Mr. Santos has read 1,146 pages of his book. He has 378 pages left to read. How many pages are in the book?

_____

Name _____

Multiply 2-Digit Numbers by 1-Digit Numbers

Essential Question What strategies can you use to find products of 2-digit numbers and 1-digit numbers?

Learning Objective You will use place value strategies such as partial products and regrouping to multiply a 2-digit number by a 1-digit number.

🔑 Unlock the Problem (Real World)

Sam has 3 boxes of crayons. Each box holds 24 crayons. How many crayons does Sam have in all?

You can model the problem using base-ten blocks.
Multiply. 3×24

🔓 Activity 1 Use place value and partial products.

Materials ■ base-ten blocks

	MODEL	THINK AND RECORD
STEP 1		Model 3 groups of 24. Multiply the tens.

$$\begin{array}{r} 2\,4 \\ \times\ \ 3 \\ \hline \end{array}$$
3×2 tens

	MODEL	THINK AND RECORD
STEP 2		Multiply the ones.

$$\begin{array}{r} 2\,4 \\ \times\ \ 3 \\ \hline \end{array}$$
3×4 ones

	MODEL	THINK AND RECORD
STEP 3		Add to find the product.

$$\begin{array}{r} 2\,4 \\ \times\ \ 3 \\ \hline 6\,0 \\ +1\,2 \\ \hline \end{array}$$
3×2 tens
3×4 ones

So, Sam has _____ crayons in all.

Activity 2 Use place value and regrouping.

Materials ■ base-ten blocks

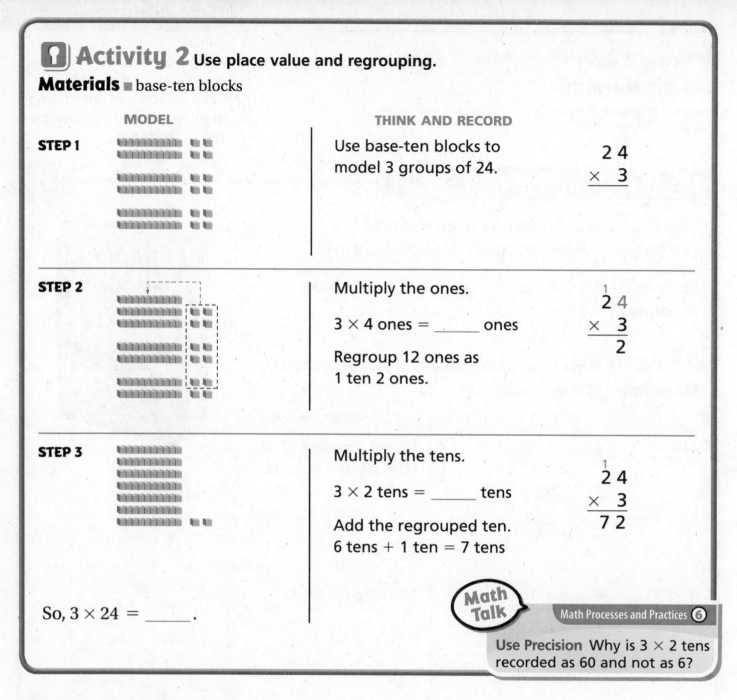

	MODEL	THINK AND RECORD	
STEP 1		Use base-ten blocks to model 3 groups of 24.	$\begin{array}{r} 2\,4 \\ \times\quad 3 \\ \hline \end{array}$
STEP 2		Multiply the ones. 3×4 ones = _____ ones Regroup 12 ones as 1 ten 2 ones.	$\begin{array}{r} \overset{1}{2}\,4 \\ \times\quad 3 \\ \hline 2 \end{array}$
STEP 3		Multiply the tens. 3×2 tens = _____ tens Add the regrouped ten. 6 tens + 1 ten = 7 tens	$\begin{array}{r} \overset{1}{2}\,4 \\ \times\quad 3 \\ \hline 7\,2 \end{array}$

So, $3 \times 24 =$ _____.

Math Talk

Math Processes and Practices ⑥

Use Precision Why is 3×2 tens recorded as 60 and not as 6?

Try This! Multiply. 5×39

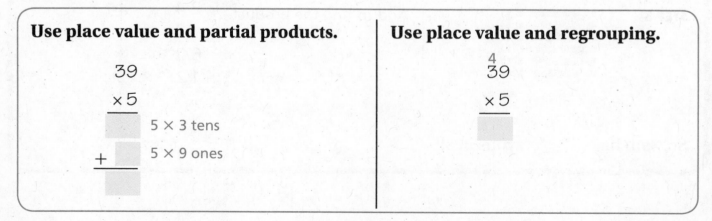

Use place value and partial products.	Use place value and regrouping.
$\begin{array}{r} 39 \\ \times 5 \\ \hline \end{array}$ _____ 5×3 tens + _____ 5×9 ones	$\begin{array}{r} \overset{4}{39} \\ \times 5 \\ \hline \end{array}$

Name _____

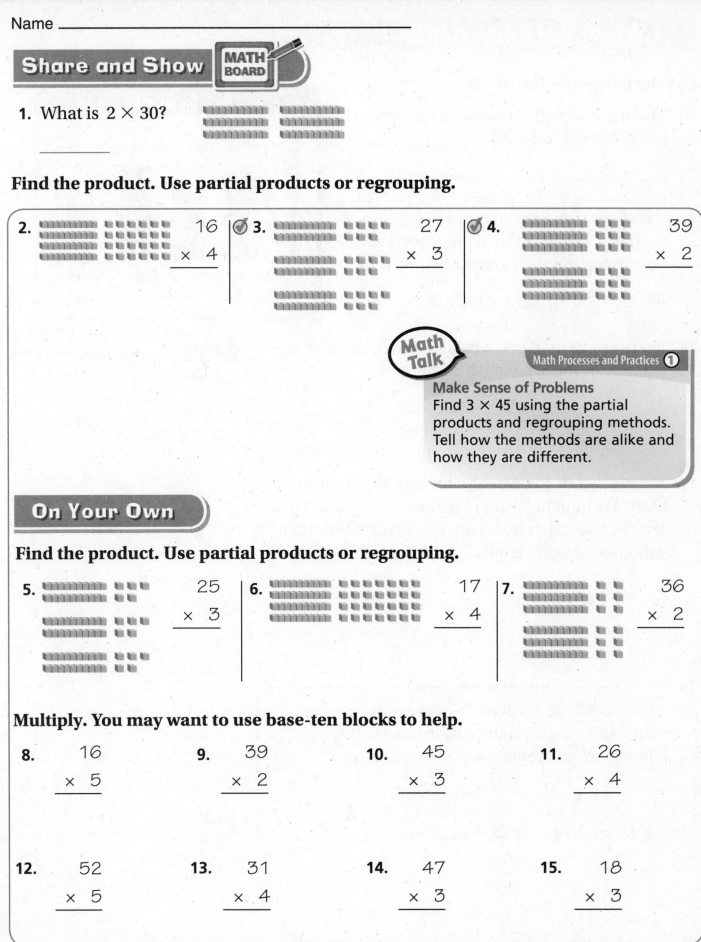

Share and Show MATH BOARD

1. What is 2×30?

_____

Find the product. Use partial products or regrouping.

2.
$$\begin{array}{r} 16 \\ \times\ 4 \end{array}$$

3.
$$\begin{array}{r} 27 \\ \times\ 3 \end{array}$$

4.
$$\begin{array}{r} 39 \\ \times\ 2 \end{array}$$

Math Talk

Math Processes and Practices ①

Make Sense of Problems
Find 3×45 using the partial products and regrouping methods. Tell how the methods are alike and how they are different.

On Your Own

Find the product. Use partial products or regrouping.

5.
$$\begin{array}{r} 25 \\ \times\ 3 \end{array}$$

6.
$$\begin{array}{r} 17 \\ \times\ 4 \end{array}$$

7.
$$\begin{array}{r} 36 \\ \times\ 2 \end{array}$$

Multiply. You may want to use base-ten blocks to help.

8.
$$\begin{array}{r} 16 \\ \times\ 5 \end{array}$$

9.
$$\begin{array}{r} 39 \\ \times\ 2 \end{array}$$

10.
$$\begin{array}{r} 45 \\ \times\ 3 \end{array}$$

11.
$$\begin{array}{r} 26 \\ \times\ 4 \end{array}$$

12.
$$\begin{array}{r} 52 \\ \times\ 5 \end{array}$$

13.
$$\begin{array}{r} 31 \\ \times\ 4 \end{array}$$

14.
$$\begin{array}{r} 47 \\ \times\ 3 \end{array}$$

15.
$$\begin{array}{r} 18 \\ \times\ 3 \end{array}$$

Problem Solving • Applications

Use the bar graph for 16–18.

16. There are 16 pencils in each box. How many pencils are in all?

_____

17. **GO DEEPER** There are 20 tubes of paint in each box. If each tube of paint costs $4, how much did the paint cost altogether?

_____

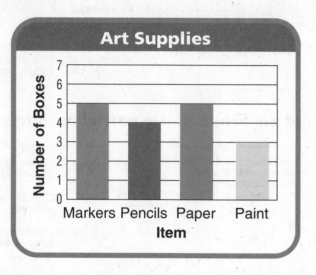

Art Supplies

18. There are 12 markers in each box. Are there more markers or more pencils? **Explain.**

_____

_____

WRITE ▸ Math • **Show Your Work**

19. **WRITE** ▸ Math Mr. Dawson invited 80 people to a party. He bought 5 bags of balloons as favors. There are 17 balloons in each bag. Will there be enough balloons for every guest? **Explain.**

_____

_____

20. **THINK SMARTER** A third-grade class went on a field trip. There were 26 students in each of 3 groups. How many students went on the field trip?

A 29 students   **C** 78 students

B 68 students   **D** 84 students

Multiply 2-Digit Numbers by 1-Digit Numbers

Learning Objective You will use place value strategies such as partial products and regrouping to multiply a 2-digit number by a 1-digit number.

Find the product. Use partial products or regrouping.

1.
$$\begin{array}{r} 46 \\ \times\ 3 \\ \hline 138 \end{array}$$

2.
$$\begin{array}{r} 32 \\ \times\ 5 \\ \hline \end{array}$$

3.
$$\begin{array}{r} \$55 \\ \times\ 2 \\ \hline \end{array}$$

4.
$$\begin{array}{r} 67 \\ \times\ 4 \\ \hline \end{array}$$

5.
$$\begin{array}{r} 37 \\ \times\ 3 \\ \hline \end{array}$$

6.
$$\begin{array}{r} \$18 \\ \times\ 4 \\ \hline \end{array}$$

7.
$$\begin{array}{r} 83 \\ \times\ 5 \\ \hline \end{array}$$

8.
$$\begin{array}{r} 95 \\ \times\ 2 \\ \hline \end{array}$$

9.
$$\begin{array}{r} 94 \\ \times\ 5 \\ \hline \end{array}$$

10.
$$\begin{array}{r} 57 \\ \times\ 4 \\ \hline \end{array}$$

11.
$$\begin{array}{r} 72 \\ \times\ 3 \\ \hline \end{array}$$

12.
$$\begin{array}{r} \$79 \\ \times\ 2 \\ \hline \end{array}$$

Problem Solving Real World

13. Sharon is 54 inches tall. A tree in her backyard is 4 times taller than she is. The height of the floor in her treehouse is twice Sharon's height. What is the difference, in inches, between the height of the top of the tree and the height of the floor of the treehouse?

_____

14. **WRITE** ▸Math Describe one way you can find the number of stickers in 4 packs of 48 stickers.

_____

_____

Lesson Check

1. A ferryboat makes 4 trips from the mainland to an island each day. The ferry can hold 88 people. If the ferry is full on each trip, how many passengers are carried by ferry each day?

   _____

2. Julian counted the number of times he drove across a 5-mile bridge while vacationing at the beach. He crossed the bridge 34 times. How many miles in all did Julian drive crossing the bridge?

   _____

Spiral Review

3. What rule can you write to describe the pattern in the table?

Input	72	64	51	45	39	20
Output	65	57	44	38	32	13

   _____

4. What two numbers come next in the pattern?

   4, 9, 14, 19, 24, 29, ■, ■

   _____

5. Name the pattern core.

   24, 42, 88, 24, 42, 88, 24, 42, 88, 24, 42, 88, 24, 42

   _____

6. A petting zoo had more than 3,654 visitors in the summer. How many visitors could have gone to the exhibit?

   _____

Write and Solve Practical Problems

Essential Question How can you use the four operations to write single-step and multi-step practical problems?

Learning Objective You will write and solve practical problems using all four operations.

⚿ Unlock the Problem (Real World)

Writing math problems helps you become a better problem solver. You can use an existing problem, or question, as a model to help you write your own math problem. You can change the numbers or some of the information, or exchange the known and unknown information.

Dave made a table showing the average temperatures in Richmond, Virginia, for 6 months.

What is the difference in average temperature between April and May?

The average temperature in April is _____ degrees.

The average temperature in May is _____ degrees.

Subtract to find the difference. _____

So, the difference in average temperatures is _____ degrees.

Month	Average Temperature (in degrees F)
January	47
February	51
March	60
April	70
May	78
June	86

Try This! Now write your own problem by changing some of the information.

What is the difference in the average temperatures

between _____ and _____?

The average temperature in _____ is _____ degrees.

The average temperature in _____ is _____ degrees.

Subtract to find the difference. _____ − _____ = _____ degrees.

So, the difference in average temperatures is _____ degrees.

🔓 Example At the Fort Christwell Animal Park, Zoo Chow is sold for $5 a bag. On Saturday, 95 bags were sold, and on Sunday 90 bags were sold. How much more money was made on Saturday than on Sunday?

Multiply to find how much money was made on Saturday.

_____ × _____ = _____

Multiply to find how much money was made on Sunday.

_____ × _____ = _____

Subtract to find the difference. _____ − _____ = _____

So, the zoo made _____ more on Zoo Chow on Saturday than on Sunday.

Math Talk

Math Processes and Practices ❶

Reasoning Explain how you can write a new problem by changing the numbers in an exisiting problem.

Try This! **Now write your own problem by changing the numbers or the known and unknown information.**

Zoo Chow is available to buy at the Fort Christwell Animal Park. Each bag sells for $5. On Saturday and Sunday the zoo made a total of $925 from Zoo Chow. 95 bags were sold Saturday. How much money was made from Zoo Chow on Sunday?

The total sold both days is _____.

On Saturday, _____ bags were sold.

Multiply to find the amount of money made on Saturday. _____ × _____ = _____

Subtract the amount of money earned on Saturday from the total amount

of money earned. _____ − _____ = _____

So, the zoo made _____ from Zoo Chow on Sunday.

Name _____

Solve.

Special tours are available to visitors at the Virginia Living Museum. On Friday, 334 people took the tour. On Saturday, 409 people took the tour. On Sunday, 227 people took the tour.

1. How many more visitors took the tour on Saturday than on Sunday?

_____

2. **Look at Problem 1.**

Write and solve a similar problem by changing the days that are compared.

How many more visitors took the tour on _____ than on _____?

_____

_____

3. **Look at Problem 1.**

Write a similar problem by changing the numbers or the known and unknown information.

There were _____ visitors on Sunday. There were _____ more visitors on Saturday than on Sunday. How many visitors were there on Saturday? _____

Solve the problem. Then write a similar problem by changing the numbers or some of the information or exchanging the known and unknown information.

4. Miranda writes short stories. She wrote 9 stories each week for 10 weeks. How many short stories did she complete?

_____

_____

_____

_____

Problem Solving • Applications Real World

The local bakery sells their muffins three days a week. The table shows the number of muffins they sold in one week.

Muffin	Friday	Saturday	Sunday
Blueberry	36	56	40
Banana	36	48	50
Cinnamon	27	40	54
Zucchini	38	25	20

4. How many muffins were sold on Friday?

_____

_____

5. Pose a Problem Look at Problem 4. Write a similar problem by changing either the day or the type of muffin.

_____

_____

6. GO DEEPER **What's the Question?** Zac bought 4 zucchini muffins on Friday. He bought 3 more muffins on Sunday than he bought on Friday.

Possible question: _____

_____

on _____

7. THINK SMARTER   The baker wants to find how much money was earned on Sunday. Each muffin costs $4. Which set of expressions show how to find the total earned on Sunday?

(A) $40 + 50 + 54 + 20 = 164$
$164 + \$4 = \$168$

(C) $40 + 50 + 54 + 20 = 164$
$164 \div \$4 = \$41$

(B) $40 + 50 + 54 + 20 = 164$
$164 - \$4 = \$160$

(D) $40 + 50 + 54 + 20 = 164$
$164 \times \$4 = \$656$

Write and Solve Practical Problems

Solve the problem. Then write a similar problem by changing the numbers or some of the information or exchanging the known and unknown information.

Learning Objective You will write and solve practical problems using all four operations.

1. Jamal bought 8 tickets for the school play. Each ticket cost $4. How much did Jamal spend on his 8 tickets?

   _____

   _____

   _____

2. Mollie is packing bottled water for the class trip. She packed 10 bottles in each of 7 boxes. How many bottles of water did Mollie pack for the class trip?

   _____

   _____

   _____

   _____

Problem Solving Real World

3. Write a problem using this information. Then solve the problem. Sierra was selling tickets for the local theater. On Friday, she sold 183 tickets. On Saturday, she sold 267 tickets. On Sunday, she sold 145 tickets.

   _____

   _____

4. **WRITE** *Math* Write a problem using this information. Then solve the problem. Walter has 5 white mice. His dad gave him 6 more.

   _____

   _____

Lesson Check

1. Solve the problem. Then change the numbers in the problem to write and solve a new one.

Marcos bought 4 boxes of crayons. Each box has 12 crayons in it. How many crayons did Marcos buy?

_____

_____

_____

2. Solve the problem. Then change the known and unknown information to write and solve a new problem.

Danyelle bought a pack of gum for $1.27, a hair band for $2.19, and two bottles of water for $1.99. How much did she spend on all three items?

_____

_____

_____

Spiral Review

3. Paul has 63 boxes of peanuts. Each box holds 8 bags. How many bags of peanuts does Paul have?

_____

4. Sandra buys 3 dozen blueberry bagels and 4 dozen whole wheat bagels. How many bagels does Sandra buy altogether?

_____

5. Kari collected canned goods for the local food bank. Kari takes 78 boxes to the food bank. There are 9 canned goods in each box. How many canned goods, in all, did Kari take to the food bank?

_____

6. Use the rule to complete the table.

Rule: Subtract 9	
Input	Output
45	
57	48
68	
76	
83	

Write Equations to Represent Equivalent Relationships

Essential Question How can you write a number sentence to describe the relationship between two expressions using = or ≠?

Learning Objective You will write a number sentence to show the relationship between two expressions using = or ≠.

Unlock the Problem (Real World)

CONNECT You have learned that an equation is a number sentence that uses the equal sign to show that two amounts are equal. An expression is part of a number sentence that has numbers and operation signs but does not have an equal sign. Two expressions are equal **(=)** when they have the same value and not equal **(≠)** when they do not have the same value.

🔑 **Use a balance scale to represent equal expressions.**

What symbol makes the number sentence true?

$$2 \times 4 \bigcirc 2 + 6$$

STEP 1   Find the value of the first expression.

Think: 2×4

_____ groups of _____
            8

STEP 2   Find the value of the second expression.

Think: $2 + 6$

_____ + _____
         8

STEP 3   Compare the values of the expressions.

Think:

The value of 2×4 is _____ .

The value of $2 + 6$ is _____ .

The expressions have the same value.

STEP 4   Write = or ≠ to make the number sentence true.

$$2 \times 4 \bigcirc 2 + 6$$

Math Talk

Math Processes and Practices ⑦

Look for Structure How would the balance scale look if the expressions were not equal?

🔑 Examples Write a number sentence to represent two expressions that are equal or not equal.

A Simon buys 24 Fuji apples and divides them into 6 equal groups. He saves one group of apples to bake a pie. Simon also buys 9 Granny Smith apples. He gives 5 apples to a friend. He saves the rest for a pie. Does Simon save the same number of apples for each pie?

STEP 1 Write an expression to match each situation.

Fuji apples saved: _____   Granny Smith apples saved: _____

STEP 2 Find the value of each expression.

Fuji apples saved: $24 \div 6 =$ _____   Granny Smith apples saved: $9 - 5 =$ _____

STEP 3 Compare the values of the expressions.

The value of $24 \div 6$ is _____.   The value of $9 - 5$ is _____.
The expressions (do / do not) have the same value.

STEP 4 Write a number sentence to represent the expressions. _____

So, Simon does /does not save the same number of apples for each pie.

B There are 5 students making flowers at each of 3 tables. There are 7 students making bracelets at each of 2 tables. Are the same number of students making flowers as are making bracelets?

STEP 1 Write an expression to match each situation.

Students making flowers: _____   Students making bracelets: _____

STEP 2 Find the value of each expression.

Students making flowers: $3 \times 5 =$ _____   Students making bracelets: 2×7 _____

STEP 3 Compare the values of the expressions.

The value of 3×5 is _____.   The value of 2×7 is _____.
The expressions (do / do not) have the same value.

STEP 4 Write a number sentence to represent the expressions. _____

So, the same number of students are/ are not making flowers as are making bracelets.

Name _____

Use the balance scale for 1. Compare the expressions. Write = or ≠ to make the number sentence true.

1. $3 \times 3 \bigcirc 4 + 5$

2. $25 \div 5 \bigcirc 3 \times 2$ ☑ **3.** $9 \times 4 \bigcirc 8 \times 4$ **4.** $29 - 8 \bigcirc 3 \times 7$

Write +, −, ×, or ÷ and a number to make the number sentence true.

☑ **5.** $23 - 5 = 6$ _____   **6.** $17 + 5 \neq 6$ _____

Math Talk Math Processes and Practices ①

Analyze Explain how you completed the expression in Exercise 5.

On Your Own

Compare the expressions. Write = or ≠ to make the number sentence true.

7. $27 \div 3 \bigcirc 4 + 5$ **8.** $15 - 8 \bigcirc 32 \div 4$ **9.** $35 \div 7 \bigcirc 24 - 19$

10. $7 \times 5 \bigcirc 36 \div 6$ **11.** $9 \times 5 \bigcirc 57 - 12$ **12.** $8 + 3 \bigcirc 36 - 24$

Write +, −, ×, or ÷ and a number to make the number sentence true.

13. $10 - 3 = 56$ _____   **14.** $40 - 4 \neq 7$ _____

15. $6 \times 6 \neq 19$ _____   **16.** $27 + 36 = 7$ _____

Complete the expression to make the equation true. Write numbers and +, −, ×, or ÷.

17. $6 + 8 = $ _____ $\bigcirc$ _____   **18.** $41 - 5 = $ _____ $\bigcirc$ _____

19. $42 \div 6 = $ _____ $\bigcirc$ _____   **20.** $9 \times 3 = $ _____ $\bigcirc$ _____

Problem Solving · Applications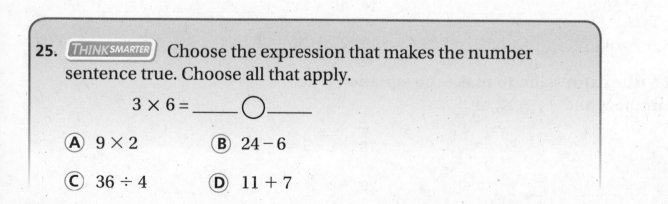

21. Jade baked a total of 32 oatmeal cookies with 8 cookies in each batch. Sofia baked a total of 30 chocolate chip cookies with 6 cookies in each batch. Did both girls bake the same number of batches? Write a number sentence using = or ≠ to explain.

_____

_____

22. Write a Problem Look at Problem 21 and write a similar problem which shows that the number of batches of cookies Jade and Sofia baked is equal. Write a number sentence using = or ≠ to explain.

_____

_____

_____

23. Sam wrote a number sentence on the board. He accidentally erased part of the sentence. Write an expression which makes Sam's number sentence true.

$$56 \div 7 = \underline{\quad} \bigcirc \underline{\quad}$$

24. Sense or Nonsense? Benjamin said the number sentence he wrote is true. Does his statement make sense? Explain your answer.

$$44 - 27 = 3 \times 9$$

_____

25. THINK SMARTER Choose the expression that makes the number sentence true. Choose all that apply.

$$3 \times 6 = \underline{\quad} \bigcirc \underline{\quad}$$

Ⓐ 9 × 2   Ⓑ 24 − 6

Ⓒ 36 ÷ 4   Ⓓ 11 + 7

Name _____

Algebra • Write Expressions to Represent Equivalent Relationships

Learning Objective You will write a number sentence to show the relationship between two expressions using = or ≠.

Compare the expressions. Write = or ≠ to make the number sentence true.

1. $36 \div 9 \; \boxed{=} \; 2 \times 2$

2. $22 - 7 \; \bigcirc \; 7 + 8$

3. $24 + 6 \; \bigcirc \; 8 \times 4$

4. $21 \div 3 \; \bigcirc \; 4 \times 2$

5. $19 + 8 \; \bigcirc \; 46 - 20$

6. $17 - 3 \; \bigcirc \; 3 + 11$

Write +, −, ×, or ÷ and a number to make the number sentence true.

7. $24 \div 8 = 52$ _____

8. $19 + 6 \neq 4$ _____

9. $8 \times 9 = 19$ _____

10. $43 - 17 \neq 5$ _____

Complete the expression to make the equation true. Write numbers and +, −, ×, or ÷.

11. $48 \div 8 =$ ____ $\bigcirc$ ____

12. $21 + 49 =$ ____ $\bigcirc$ ____

13. $8 \times 4 =$ ____ $\bigcirc$ ____

14. $63 \div 7 =$ ____ $\bigcirc$ ____

Problem Solving (Real World)

15. A garden center sells trays of flowers. One tray has 2 rows of 8 flowers. Another tray has 3 rows of 5 flowers. Do both trays have the same number of flowers? Write a number sentence using = or ≠ to explain.

_____

_____

_____

16. **WRITE** ▸ *Math* Explain how you choose which sign to use when comparing two expressions. Use the symbols = and ≠ in your explanation.

_____

_____

_____

Lesson Check

1. PJ buys 4 bags of apples. There are 6 apples in each bag. Scott buys 3 bags of pears. There are 8 pears in each bag. Do PJ and Scott buy the same number of pieces of fruit? Write a number sentence using = or ≠ to explain.

_____

_____

2. Amir has 54 cups of dog food. He feeds his dogs 6 cups of food each day. Hannah has 56 cups of dog food. She feeds her dogs 7 cups of dog food each day. Will Amir and Hannah's dog food last the same number of days? Write a number sentence using = or ≠ to explain.

_____

_____

Spiral Review

3. The third-grade classes went on buses for a field trip. There were 4 buses with 27 students on each bus. How many students went on the field trip?

_____

4. Name the pattern core. Then write the next two numbers.

   81, 18, 11, 81, 18, 11, 81, 18, 11, 81, 18, ■, ■

_____

5. Which two numbers come next in the pattern?

   71, 67, 63, 59, 55, 51, ■, ■

_____

6. Write a rule to describe the pattern in the table.

Input	7	12	19	28	39	52
Output	3	8	15	24	35	48

_____

Name _____

Fractions and Mixed Numbers

Essential Question When might you use a fraction greater than 1 or a mixed number?

Learning Objective You will use models to represent, name, and write mixed numbers and fractions greater than 1.

🔑 **Unlock the Problem** Real World

Sarah volunteers at an animal shelter. She feeds each kitten $\frac{1}{3}$ can of food. How many cans of food does she feed 5 kittens?

• How much food does Sarah give to each kitten?

_____

• How many kittens does she feed?

_____

🔓 **One Way** Make a model.

• Shade $\frac{1}{3}$ for the amount of food Sarah gives to each of the 5 kittens.

• Then count the number of shaded pieces.

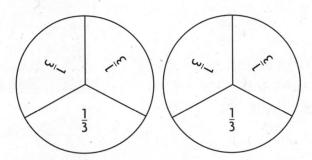

Think: $\frac{3}{3} = 1$

One whole and two-thirds are shaded.

Write: $1\frac{2}{3}$

_____ pieces are shaded.

So, _____ is shaded. $\frac{5}{3} =$ _____

The number $\frac{5}{3}$ is a fraction greater than 1. A fraction greater than 1 has a numerator that is greater than its denominator.

The number $1\frac{2}{3}$ is a mixed number. A **mixed number** has a whole number and a fraction.

So, Sarah gives 5 kittens _____, or _____, cans of food.

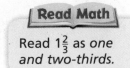

Read Math

Read $1\frac{2}{3}$ as *one and two-thirds.*

🔒 Other Ways

Ⓐ Use a number line.

Sarah walked to raise money for the animal shelter. She earned a prize for every $\frac{1}{3}$ mile she walked. If she earned 5 prizes, how many miles did Sarah walk?

- Draw a jump of $\frac{1}{3}$ on the number line.
- Continue to draw jumps until there is a jump for each prize Sarah earned.

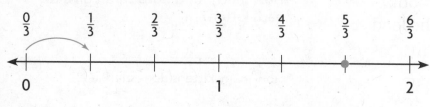

There are _____ jumps of $\frac{1}{3}$ on the number line.

There are _____ jumps past 1 on the number line.

You can say the jumps end at $\frac{5}{3}$ or $1\frac{2}{3}$ on the number line.

So, Sarah walked _____ , or _____ , miles.

Ⓑ Use a model of a group.

Daniel collects baseballs. He has collected 19 so far. He puts them in cases that hold 12 baseballs each. What part of the baseball cases has Daniel filled?

Daniel has a full case of 12 baseballs and 7 baseballs in another case.

So, _____ , or _____ , baseball cases are filled.

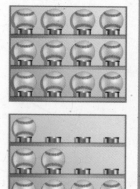

Think: 1 case = 1

Try This! Complete the mixed number and the fraction greater than 1 to name the part filled.

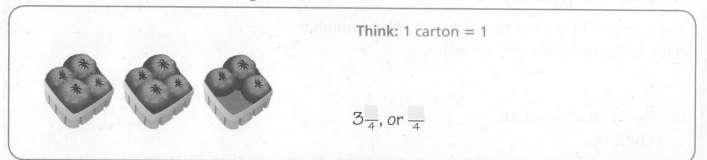

Think: 1 carton = 1

$$3\frac{\square}{4}, \text{ or } \frac{\square}{4}$$

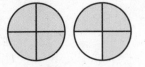 **Share and Show** MATH BOARD

1. Each circle is 1 whole. Write a mixed number for the parts that are shaded. _____

   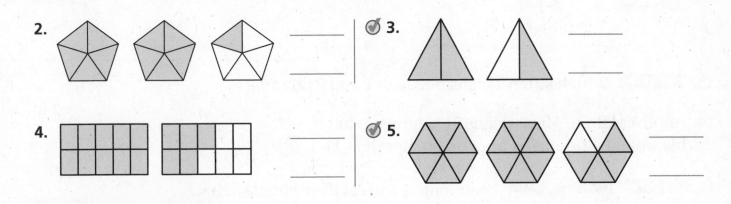

   Think: There are $\frac{7}{4}$ in all.

Math Talk — Math Processes and Practices 6

Explain how you know whether a fraction can be renamed as a mixed number.

Each shape is 1 whole. Write a mixed number and a fraction greater than 1 for the parts that are shaded.

2. _____

3. _____

4. _____

5. _____

On Your Own

Each shape is 1 whole. Write a mixed number and a fraction greater than 1 for the parts that are shaded.

6. _____

7. _____

Use the number line to write the fraction greater than 1 as a mixed number.

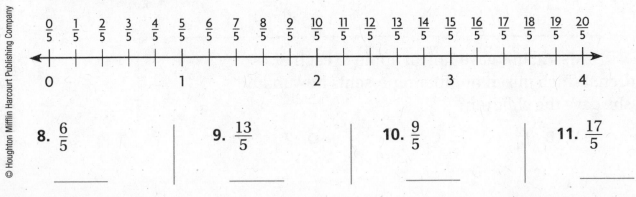

8. $\frac{6}{5}$ _____

9. $\frac{13}{5}$ _____

10. $\frac{9}{5}$ _____

11. $\frac{17}{5}$ _____

Problem Solving • Applications (Real World)

Use the table for 12–13.

Weights of Kittens	
Name	Weight (in pounds)
Timber	$\frac{11}{4}$
Kally	$\frac{9}{6}$
Tabby	$\frac{10}{3}$

12. The table shows the weights of some kittens. Shade the model to show Timber's weight in pounds. Then write the weight as a mixed number.

_____

13. **GO DEEPER** Which kitten weighs between 1 and 2 pounds? _____

14. Another kitten, Max, weighs $3\frac{1}{2}$ pounds. What is his weight written as a fraction greater than 1? _____

15. **GO DEEPER** **WRITE** ▸*Math* Buttercup is a cat at the animal shelter. She weighs $2\frac{5}{8}$ pounds. Is her weight closer to 2 pounds or 3 pounds? Explain.

_____

_____

16. Mrs. Randolph brings muffins to the workers at the shelter. Write a mixed number and fraction greater than 1 to name the part of the muffin pans filled.

_____

Think: 1 pan = 1

17. **THINK SMARTER** Ms. Adams gave $\frac{1}{4}$ of an apple to each of 10 children. Which mixed number represents how many apples she gave the children?

Ⓐ $1\frac{4}{10}$ Ⓑ $1\frac{2}{4}$ Ⓒ $2\frac{1}{4}$ Ⓓ $2\frac{2}{4}$

Fractions and Mixed Numbers

Learning Objective You will use models to represent, name, and write mixed numbers and fractions greater than 1.

Each shape is 1 whole. Write a mixed number and a fraction greater than 1 for the parts that are shaded.

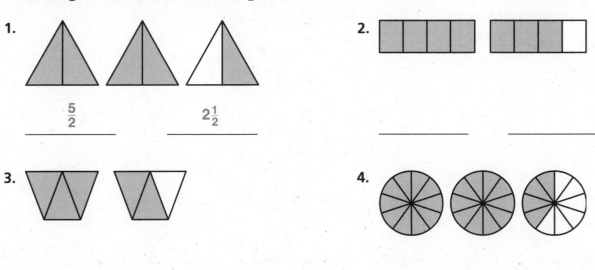

1. $\dfrac{5}{2}$ _____ $2\dfrac{1}{2}$ _____

2. _____

3. _____ _____

4. _____ _____

Use the number line to write the fraction greater than 1 as a mixed number.

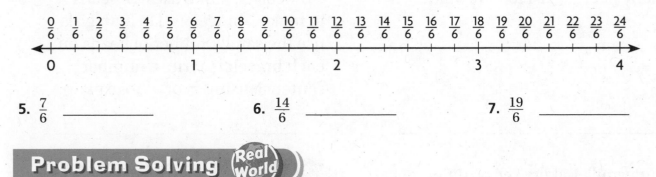

5. $\dfrac{7}{6}$ _____ 6. $\dfrac{14}{6}$ _____ 7. $\dfrac{19}{6}$ _____

Problem Solving Real World

8. Rachel gave $\frac{1}{4}$ of a pie to each of 5 friends. How many pies did she give to her friends in all? Write the number of pies she gave as a mixed number and as a fraction greater than 1.

9. Mr. Knox has these cartons of eggs left after baking a cake. Write a mixed number and a fraction greater than 1 to name the part filled.

Think: 1 carton = 1

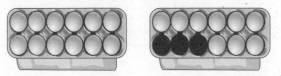

_____ _____

Lesson Check

1. Each shape is 1 whole. What mixed number is modeled by the shaded parts?

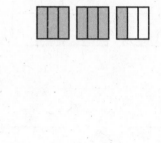

   Ⓐ $1\frac{1}{3}$

   Ⓑ $2\frac{1}{3}$

   Ⓒ $2\frac{1}{2}$

   Ⓓ $2\frac{2}{3}$

2. Alex's family ate $1\frac{7}{8}$ same-size pizzas for dinner. Which shows this mixed number written as a fraction greater than 1?

   Ⓐ $\frac{9}{8}$

   Ⓑ $\frac{15}{8}$

   Ⓒ $\frac{16}{8}$

   Ⓓ $\frac{17}{8}$

Spiral Review

3. A report folder holds 24 pages. How many pages will 4 folders hold?

4. Carol uses 28 beads to make 4 bracelets. Jamie uses 27 beads to make 3 bracelets. Do both girls use the same number of beads on each bracelet? Write a number sentence using = or ≠ to explain.

5. Buttermilk Bakery sells 4 different flavors of muffins every day. The owner recorded the number of muffins sold yesterday. Draw a conclusion about the blueberry muffins sold.

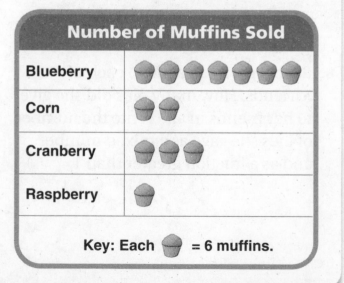

Number of Muffins Sold	
Blueberry	🧁🧁🧁🧁🧁🧁🧁
Corn	🧁🧁
Cranberry	🧁🧁🧁
Raspberry	🧁

Key: Each 🧁 = 6 muffins.

Name _____

Compare Fractions Using Benchmarks

Essential Question How can you use models and benchmarks to compare fractions?

Learning Objective You will use models and the benchmarks 0, $\frac{1}{2}$, and 1 to compare fractions.

Benchmarks are numbers that are easy to work with. The numbers 0, $\frac{1}{2}$, and 1 are benchmarks that make it easier for you to compare fractions.

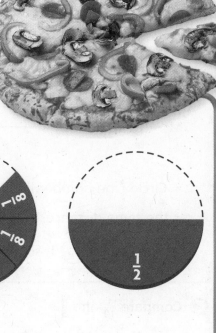

🔑 Unlock the Problem · Real World

Ava ordered a pizza. She ate $\frac{5}{8}$ of it. Did Ava eat more than or less than $\frac{1}{2}$ of her pizza?

🔓 **Use benchmarks and fraction circles.**

Ⓐ Compare $\frac{5}{8}$ and $\frac{1}{2}$.

Ava ate _____ of her pizza.

Is $\frac{5}{8}$ greater than or less than $\frac{1}{2}$? _____

So, Ava ate _____ $\frac{1}{2}$ of her pizza.

_____

Skylar ate $\frac{7}{8}$ of her pizza. Did Skylar eat more than or less than 1 whole pizza?

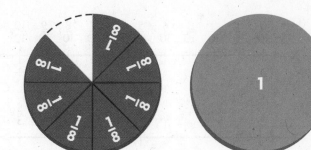

Ⓑ Compare $\frac{7}{8}$ and 1.

Skylar ate _____ of her pizza.

Is $\frac{7}{8}$ greater than or less than 1? _____

So, Skylar ate _____ 1 whole pizza.

_____

Aiden ate $\frac{1}{8}$ of his pizza. Did Aiden eat almost none of his pizza?

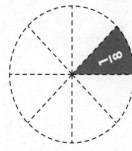

Ⓒ Compare $\frac{1}{8}$ and 0.

Aiden ate _____ of his pizza.

Is $\frac{1}{8}$ a little more than 0? _____

So, Aiden ate _____ of his pizza.

Examples Use benchmarks and number lines.

A Compare $\frac{4}{5}$ and $\frac{3}{3}$.

- Circle $\frac{4}{5}$ on number line **L**.

$\frac{4}{5}$ is to the left of 1, so $\frac{4}{5}$ $\bigcirc$ 1.

- Circle $\frac{3}{3}$ on number line **M**.

$\frac{3}{3}$ the same distance from 0 as 1, so $\frac{3}{3}$ $\bigcirc$ 1.

$\frac{4}{5}$ $\bigcirc$ 1 and $\frac{3}{3}$ $\bigcirc$ 1, so $\frac{4}{5}$ $\bigcirc$ $\frac{3}{3}$.

B Compare $\frac{2}{6}$ and $\frac{3}{4}$.

- Circle $\frac{2}{6}$ on number line **S**.

$\frac{2}{6}$ is to the left of $\frac{1}{2}$, so $\frac{2}{6}$ $\bigcirc$ $\frac{1}{2}$.

- Circle $\frac{3}{4}$ on number line **T**.

$\frac{3}{4}$ is to the right of $\frac{1}{2}$, so $\frac{3}{4}$ $\bigcirc$ $\frac{1}{2}$.

$\frac{2}{6}$ $\bigcirc$ $\frac{1}{2}$ and $\frac{3}{4}$ $\bigcirc$ $\frac{1}{2}$, so $\frac{2}{6}$ $\bigcirc$ $\frac{3}{4}$.

C Compare $\frac{1}{10}$ and $\frac{3}{5}$.

- Circle $\frac{1}{10}$ on the number line **X**.

Is $\frac{1}{10}$ closest to 0 , $\frac{1}{2}$, or 1?_____

- Circle $\frac{3}{5}$ on the number line **Y**. Is $\frac{3}{5}$ closest

to 0, $\frac{1}{2}$, or 1? _____

Since $0 < \frac{1}{2}$, now you know the greater

fraction is closest to $\frac{1}{2}$.

So, $\frac{1}{10}$ $\bigcirc$ $\frac{1}{5}$.

Use reasoning.

D Compare $\frac{3}{8}$ and $\frac{5}{6}$.

- First, look at $\frac{3}{8}$. Think: $\frac{1}{2}$ of 8 = 4

So, $\frac{4}{8}$ is the same as $\frac{1}{2}$. Now you know

$\frac{3}{8}$ $\bigcirc$ $\frac{1}{2}$.

- Then look at $\frac{5}{6}$. Think: $\frac{1}{2}$ of 6 = 3

So, $\frac{3}{6}$ is the same as $\frac{1}{2}$. Now you know

$\frac{5}{6}$ $\bigcirc$ $\frac{1}{2}$.

So, $\frac{3}{8}$ $\bigcirc$ $\frac{5}{6}$.

- If the numerator *is less than* half the denominator, the fraction is less than $\frac{1}{2}$.
- If the numerator *is greater than* half the denominator, the fraction is greater than $\frac{1}{2}$.

Math Talk

Math Processes and Practices **6**

Explain how you know that a fraction is less than $\frac{1}{2}$ when the numerator is less than half the denominator.

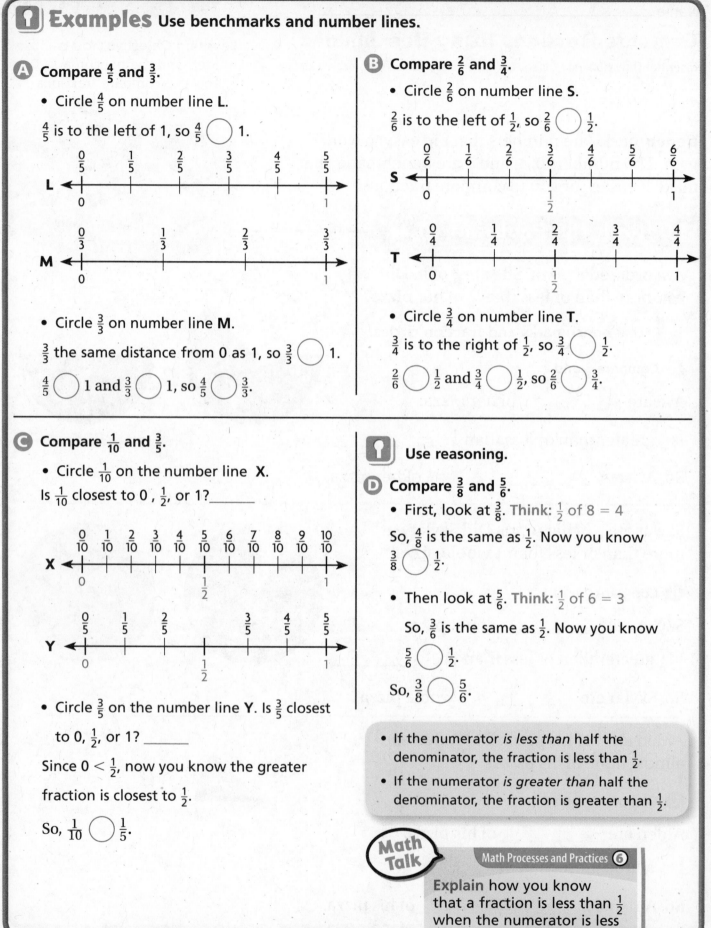

Name _____

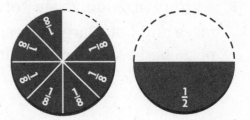

1. Use the models to compare $\frac{7}{8}$ and $\frac{1}{2}$.

    Is $\frac{7}{8}$ equal to or not equal to $\frac{1}{2}$? _____

    Is $\frac{7}{8}$ greater than or less than $\frac{1}{2}$? _____

Use the benchmarks on the number line to help you compare. Write < or >.

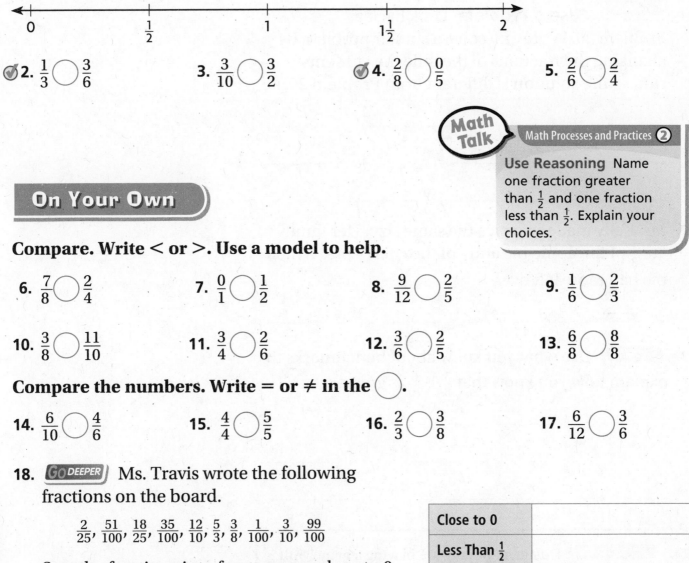

2. $\frac{1}{3}$ ◯ $\frac{3}{6}$

3. $\frac{3}{10}$ ◯ $\frac{3}{2}$

4. $\frac{2}{8}$ ◯ $\frac{0}{5}$

5. $\frac{2}{6}$ ◯ $\frac{2}{4}$

Math Talk Math Processes and Practices ②

Use Reasoning Name one fraction greater than $\frac{1}{2}$ and one fraction less than $\frac{1}{2}$. Explain your choices.

On Your Own

Compare. Write < or >. Use a model to help.

6. $\frac{7}{8}$ ◯ $\frac{2}{4}$

7. $\frac{0}{1}$ ◯ $\frac{1}{2}$

8. $\frac{9}{12}$ ◯ $\frac{2}{5}$

9. $\frac{1}{6}$ ◯ $\frac{2}{3}$

10. $\frac{3}{8}$ ◯ $\frac{11}{10}$

11. $\frac{3}{4}$ ◯ $\frac{2}{6}$

12. $\frac{3}{6}$ ◯ $\frac{2}{5}$

13. $\frac{6}{8}$ ◯ $\frac{8}{8}$

Compare the numbers. Write = or ≠ in the ◯.

14. $\frac{6}{10}$ ◯ $\frac{4}{6}$

15. $\frac{4}{4}$ ◯ $\frac{5}{5}$

16. $\frac{2}{3}$ ◯ $\frac{3}{8}$

17. $\frac{6}{12}$ ◯ $\frac{3}{6}$

18. **GO DEEPER** Ms. Travis wrote the following fractions on the board.

    $$\frac{2}{25}, \frac{51}{100}, \frac{18}{25}, \frac{35}{100}, \frac{12}{10}, \frac{5}{3}, \frac{3}{8}, \frac{1}{100}, \frac{3}{10}, \frac{99}{100}$$

    Sort the fractions into four groups: close to 0, less than $\frac{1}{2}$, greater than $\frac{1}{2}$, and greater than 1. Complete the chart. Some fractions may be used more than once.

Close to 0	
Less Than $\frac{1}{2}$	
Greater Than $\frac{1}{2}$	
Greater Than 1	

Problem Solving · Applications (Real World)

19. A group of students ate $\frac{5}{8}$ of a large pepperoni pizza and $\frac{1}{4}$ of a large cheese pizza. Which pizza had a smaller part left?

_____

20. Tyrone runs $\frac{4}{10}$ mile. Lena runs $\frac{3}{4}$ mile. Who runs farther? _____

21. GO DEEPER **Pose a Problem** Look back at Problem 20. Write and solve a similar problem by changing the fractions of the mile the students run, so the solution is different from Problem 20.

_____

_____

_____

22. Ms. Kelly made two pies the same size. Her family ate $\frac{1}{3}$ of the apple pie and $\frac{3}{4}$ of the cherry pie. Which pie had more left over?

_____

_____

23. GO DEEPER Use what you know about benchmarks to explain how you know that $\frac{5}{8} + \frac{6}{10}$ is greater than 1.

_____

_____

_____

24. THINK SMARTER Dustin and Claire are playing a game with fraction pieces. Which statement is NOT correct?

(A) $\frac{5}{6} < \frac{1}{2}$ (C) $\frac{5}{6} > 0$

(B) $\frac{3}{6} = \frac{1}{2}$ (D) $\frac{5}{6} < 1$

Name _____

Compare Fractions Using Benchmarks

Learning Objective You will use models and the benchmarks 0, $\frac{1}{2}$, and 1 to compare fractions.

Use the benchmarks on the number line to help you compare. Write < or >.

1. Compare $\frac{2}{8}$ and $\frac{3}{4}$.

   $\frac{2}{8}$ $\left(<\right)$ $\frac{3}{4}$

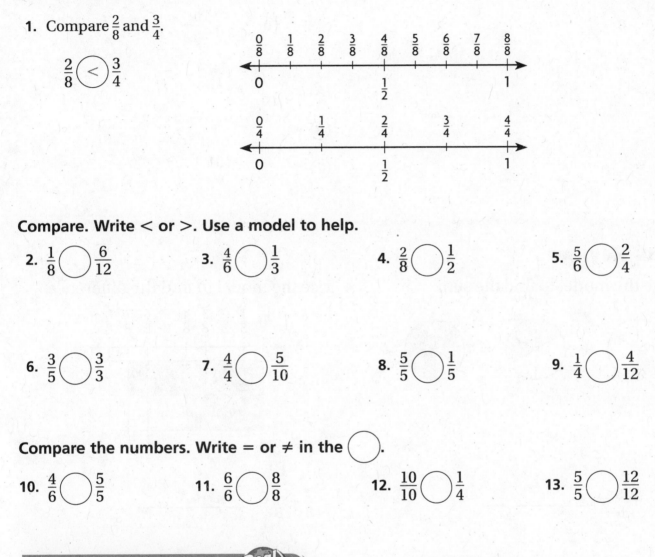

Compare. Write < or >. Use a model to help.

2. $\frac{1}{8}$ ◯ $\frac{6}{12}$

3. $\frac{4}{6}$ ◯ $\frac{1}{3}$

4. $\frac{2}{8}$ ◯ $\frac{1}{2}$

5. $\frac{5}{6}$ ◯ $\frac{2}{4}$

6. $\frac{3}{5}$ ◯ $\frac{3}{3}$

7. $\frac{4}{4}$ ◯ $\frac{5}{10}$

8. $\frac{5}{5}$ ◯ $\frac{1}{5}$

9. $\frac{1}{4}$ ◯ $\frac{4}{12}$

Compare the numbers. Write = or ≠ in the ◯.

10. $\frac{4}{6}$ ◯ $\frac{5}{5}$

11. $\frac{6}{6}$ ◯ $\frac{8}{8}$

12. $\frac{10}{10}$ ◯ $\frac{1}{4}$

13. $\frac{5}{5}$ ◯ $\frac{12}{12}$

Problem Solving Real World

14. Faith ran $\frac{3}{8}$ mile. Carly ran $\frac{3}{4}$ mile. Which is the greater distance?

_____

15. Ryan finished $\frac{1}{3}$ of his art project on Monday. Ethan finished $\frac{1}{2}$ of his art project on Monday. Who finished more of his art project on Monday?

_____

Lesson Check

1. Which symbol makes the statement true?

$$\frac{4}{6} \bullet \frac{3}{8}$$

Ⓐ >

Ⓑ <

Ⓒ =

2. Which symbol makes the statement true?

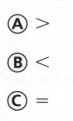

Ⓐ >

Ⓑ <

Ⓒ =

Spiral Review

3. Use the model to find the sum.

$$\frac{1}{6} + \frac{3}{6} = \underline{\hspace{2cm}}$$

4. Use the model to find the difference.

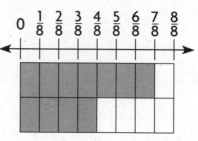

$$\frac{7}{8} - \frac{4}{8} = \underline{\hspace{2cm}}$$

5. Mr. Gregory gave $\frac{1}{4}$ of an orange to each of his 6 children. Write a mixed number and a fraction greater than 1 to name how many oranges he gave the children.

6. An outfitter rents boats. One group of 21 people wants to rent 3 boats. Another group of 24 people wants to rent 4 boats. Do both groups have the same number of people in each boat? Write a number sentence using = or ≠ to explain.

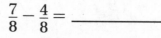

Name _____

Add and Subtract Like Fractions

Essential Question How can you solve problems that involve addition and subtraction of like fractions?

Learning Objective You will solve problems that involve addition and subtraction of like fractions.

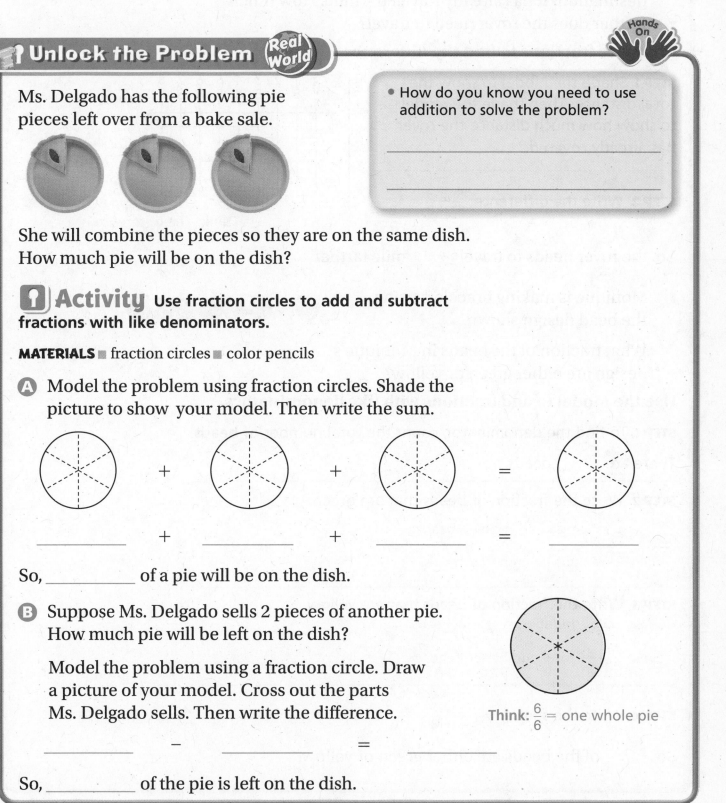

Unlock the Problem Real World

Ms. Delgado has the following pie pieces left over from a bake sale.

She will combine the pieces so they are on the same dish. How much pie will be on the dish?

- How do you know you need to use addition to solve the problem?

_____

_____

Activity Use fraction circles to add and subtract fractions with like denominators.

MATERIALS ■ fraction circles ■ color pencils

A Model the problem using fraction circles. Shade the picture to show your model. Then write the sum.

_____ + _____ + _____ = _____

So, _____ of a pie will be on the dish.

B Suppose Ms. Delgado sells 2 pieces of another pie. How much pie will be left on the dish?

Model the problem using a fraction circle. Draw a picture of your model. Cross out the parts Ms. Delgado sells. Then write the difference.

Think: $\frac{6}{6}$ = one whole pie

_____ − _____ = _____

So, _____ of the pie is left on the dish.

- How can you write $\frac{5}{6}$ as a sum of unit fractions? _____

🔓 Examples

A A lunar rover needs to travel $\frac{5}{8}$ mile to reach its destination. It has already traveled $\frac{3}{8}$ mile. How much farther does the rover need to travel?

Compare fractions to find the difference.

STEP 1 Shade the model to show the total distance. Then shade the model to show how much distance the rover has already covered.

_____

STEP 2 Write the difference. $\frac{5}{8} - \frac{3}{8} = \frac{}{8}$

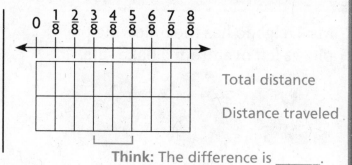

Total distance

Distance traveled

Think: The difference is _____.

So, the rover needs to travel _____ mile farther.

B Monique is making bracelets using the bead design shown.

What fraction of the beads in Monique's design are either green or yellow?

Use the model to add fractions with like denominators.

STEP 1 To find the denominator, count the total number of beads.

There are _____ beads.

_____

STEP 2 Write the fraction of beads that are green.

[ ] ⟵ —————— number of green beads

[ ] ⟵ —————— total number of beads

_____

STEP 3 Write the fraction of beads that are yellow.

[ ] ⟵ —————— number of yellow beads

[ ] ⟵ —————— total number of beads

_____

STEP 4 Write the sum. $\frac{4}{8} + \frac{1}{8} = \frac{}{8}$

So, _____ of the beads are either green or yellow.

Name _____

Use the model to write an equation.

1. Shade the model to show $\frac{3}{6} + \frac{2}{6}$.

   Write the sum. $\frac{3}{6} + \frac{2}{6} = \frac{}{6}$

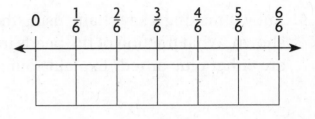

Use the model to find the sum or difference.

2. $\frac{7}{8} - \frac{4}{8} =$ _____

3. $\frac{5}{6} + \frac{1}{6} =$ _____

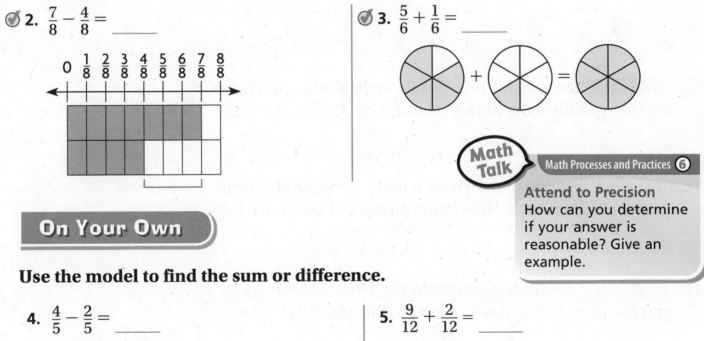

On Your Own

Math Talk Math Processes and Practices ⑥

Attend to Precision
How can you determine if your answer is reasonable? Give an example.

Use the model to find the sum or difference.

4. $\frac{4}{5} - \frac{2}{5} =$ _____

5. $\frac{9}{12} + \frac{2}{12} =$ _____

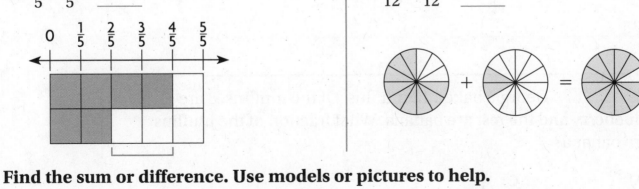

Find the sum or difference. Use models or pictures to help.

6. $\frac{7}{10} - \frac{3}{10} =$ _____

7. $\frac{2}{4} + \frac{1}{4} =$ _____

8. $\frac{2}{3} + \frac{1}{3} =$ _____

Problem Solving • Applications Real World

Use the beads for 9–10.

9. Ruby is making a key chain, using the bead design shown. What fraction of the beads in her design are either blue or red? Explain your answer.

_____

_____

10. **Pose a Problem** Use the information in Problem 9 to write a subtraction problem. Then solve.

_____

_____

_____

11. **GO DEEPER** Chaz rode his bike $\frac{4}{10}$ mile to the park. Then he rode another $\frac{7}{10}$ mile to the library. How far did Chaz bike in all?

_____

12. Inez made $\frac{3}{4}$ gallon of punch for a party. Her friends drank $\frac{2}{4}$ gallon of the punch. How much punch did Inez have left?

_____

13. **THINK SMARTER** A sum has four addends. Each addend is a unit fraction. The sum is $\frac{4}{4}$. What are the addends?

_____

14. **THINK SMARTER** Georgia baked 12 muffins. Of the muffins, 8 are blueberry and the rest are banana. What fraction of the muffins are banana?

   (A) $\frac{20}{12}$ (C) $\frac{8}{12}$

   (B) $\frac{16}{12}$ (D) $\frac{4}{12}$

Add and Subtract Like Fractions

Use the model to find the sum or difference.

Learning Objective You will solve problems that involve addition and subtraction of like fractions.

1.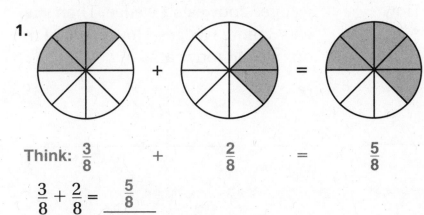

Think: $\dfrac{3}{8}$ + $\dfrac{2}{8}$ = $\dfrac{5}{8}$

$\dfrac{3}{8} + \dfrac{2}{8} = \underline{\dfrac{5}{8}}$

2.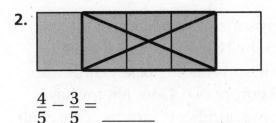

$\dfrac{4}{5} - \dfrac{3}{5} = \underline{\hspace{1cm}}$

3.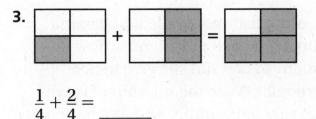

$\dfrac{1}{4} + \dfrac{2}{4} = \underline{\hspace{1cm}}$

4.

$\dfrac{2}{6} + \dfrac{3}{6} = \underline{\hspace{1cm}}$

5.

$\dfrac{10}{10} - \dfrac{6}{10} = \underline{\hspace{1cm}}$

Problem Solving Real World

6. Jake ate $\dfrac{4}{8}$ of a pizza. Millie ate $\dfrac{3}{8}$ of the same pizza. How much of the pizza was eaten by Jake and Millie?

7. **WRITE** ▸Math Draw a model that shows $\dfrac{5}{6} - \dfrac{1}{6}$ and write the difference.

Lesson Check

1. A whole pie is cut into 8 equal slices. Three of the slices are served. How much of the pie is left?

2. An orange is divided into 6 equal wedges. Jody eats 1 wedge. Then she eats 3 more wedges. How much of the orange did Jody eat?

Spiral Review

3. Carmela gave $\frac{1}{3}$ of a loaf of banana bread to each of 5 friends. How many loaves did she give to her friends? Write the number of loaves as a mixed number and as a fraction greater than 1.

4. Jeremy sorts his collection of 32 baseball cards into equal groups of 4. He sorts his 48 hockey cards into equal groups of 6. Does Jeremy have the same number of groups of baseball and hockey cards? Write a number sentence using = or ≠ to explain.

Use the picture for 5–6.

Miles is going to pull a marble out of this bag without looking. The marbles are the same shape and size.

5. Is it certain, likely, unlikely, or impossible that Miles will pull a green marble?

6. What are the possible outcomes for 1 pull?

Name _____

Count and Compare Money

Essential Question How can you count and compare total values of collections of bills and coins?

Learning Objective You will compare total values of collections of bills and coins by counting and using place value.

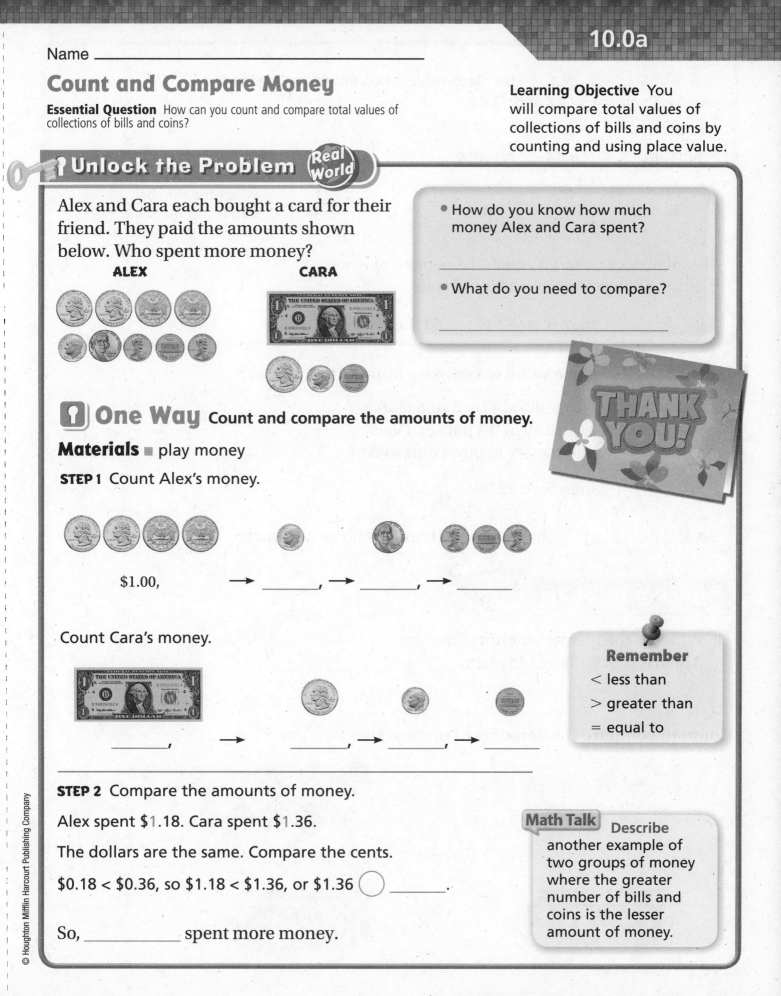

Unlock the Problem (Real World)

Alex and Cara each bought a card for their friend. They paid the amounts shown below. Who spent more money?

ALEX

CARA

- How do you know how much money Alex and Cara spent?

  _____

- What do you need to compare?

  _____

THANK YOU!

One Way Count and compare the amounts of money.

Materials ▪ play money

STEP 1 Count Alex's money.

$1.00, → _____, → _____, → _____

Count Cara's money.

_____, → _____, → _____, → _____

Remember

< less than

> greater than

= equal to

STEP 2 Compare the amounts of money.

Alex spent $1.18. Cara spent $1.36.

The dollars are the same. Compare the cents.

$0.18 < $0.36, so $1.18 < $1.36, or $1.36 ◯ _____.

So, _____ spent more money.

Math Talk Describe another example of two groups of money where the greater number of bills and coins is the lesser amount of money.

🔑 Another Way Use place value to compare the amounts of money. Compare $2.47 and $2.49.

Use a chart.

DOLLARS	·	DIMES	PENNIES
$2	·	4	7
$2	·	4	9

2 = 2   4 = 4   7 < 9

The number of dollars is equal. The number of dimes is equal. Compare the number of pennies.

7 is _____ than 9, so $2.47 ◯ $2.49.

Math Idea

When the number of digits is the same, compare digits with the greatest money value first.

Try This! Use place value to compare amounts of money.

Caleb wants to buy a milkshake. A milkshake costs $2.99. He has $2.59 in his pocket. Does Caleb have enough money to buy a milkshake?

DOLLARS	·	DIMES	PENNIES
	·		
	·		

9 is _____ than 5, so $2.99 ◯ $2.59.

___ ◯ ___   ___ ◯ ___   ___ ◯ ___

So, Caleb _____ have enough money to buy a milkshake.

Share and Show MATH BOARD

1. Which is the greater amount of money, 3 quarters or 6 dimes? Explain. _____

Count to compare the amounts of money. Use <, >, or =.

2.

_____ ◯ _____

✓ 3.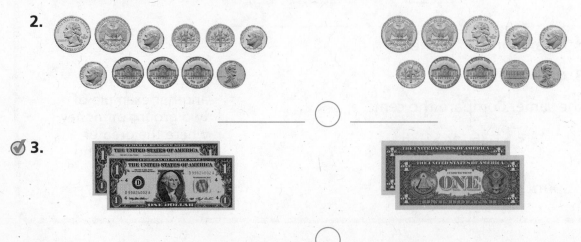

_____ ◯ _____

Name _____

**Use place value to compare the amounts of money.
Circle the greater amount.**

4. $4.00 or $0.40

5. $3.82 or $3.90

Math Talk Explain how to use place value to compare $4.58 and $4.72.

On Your Own

Count to compare the amounts of money. Use <, >, or =.

6.

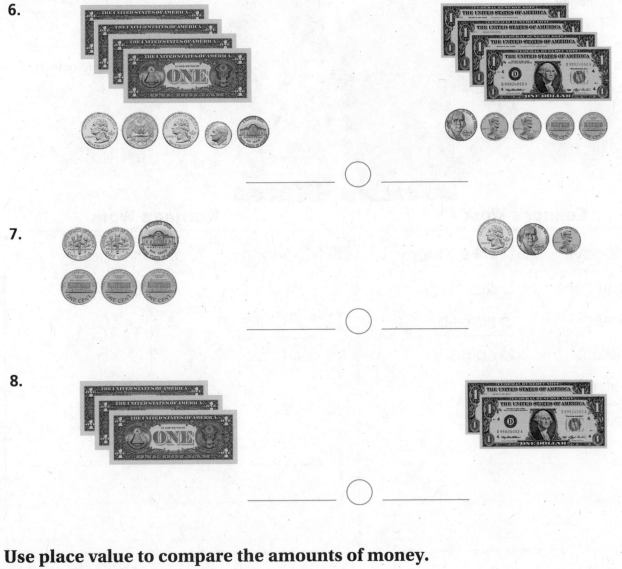

7.

_____ ◯ _____

8.

_____ ◯ _____

**Use place value to compare the amounts of money.
Circle the greater amount.**

9. $2.69 or $2.60

10. $1.05 or $0.75

11. $1.34 or $1.44

Problem Solving 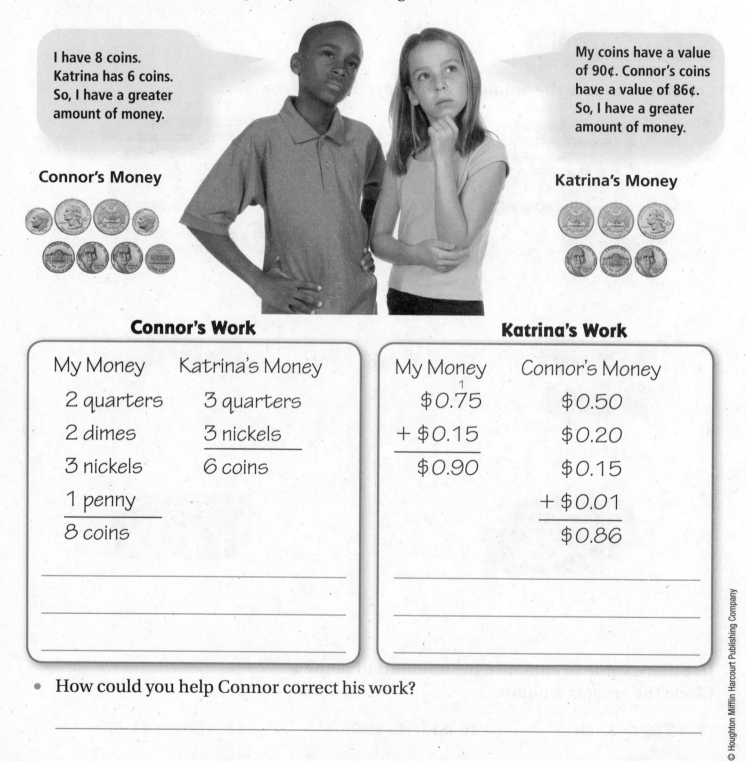Real World

What's the Error?

12. Connor and Katrina are comparing coins to find out who has the greater amount of money. Whose answer makes sense? Whose answer is nonsense? Explain your reasoning.

I have 8 coins. Katrina has 6 coins. So, I have a greater amount of money.

My coins have a value of 90¢. Connor's coins have a value of 86¢. So, I have a greater amount of money.

Connor's Money

Katrina's Money

Connor's Work

My Money	Katrina's Money
2 quarters	3 quarters
2 dimes	3 nickels
3 nickels	6 coins
1 penny	
8 coins	

Katrina's Work

My Money	Connor's Money
$0.75	$0.50
+ $0.15	$0.20
$0.90	$0.15
	+ $0.01
	$0.86

- How could you help Connor correct his work?

Count and Compare Money

Learning Objective You will compare total values of collections of bills and coins by counting and using place value.

**Count to compare the amounts of money.
Use <, >, or =.**

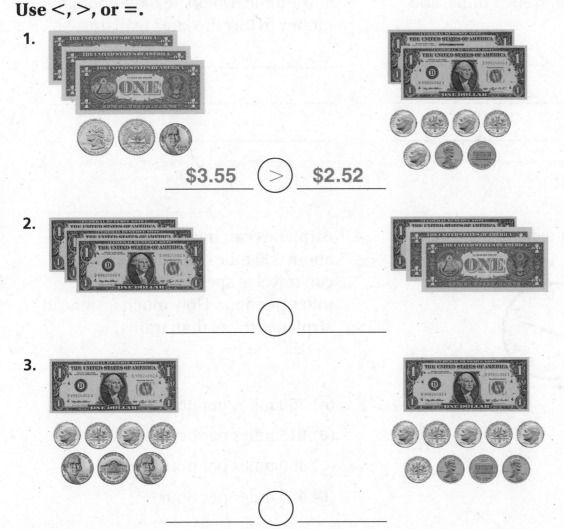

1. $3.55 $\bigcirc$> $2.52

2. _____ $\bigcirc$ _____

3. _____ $\bigcirc$ _____

Use place value to compare the amounts of money. Circle the greater amount.

4. $1.45 or $1.40

5. $2.05 or $2.50

6. $3.98 or $4.13

![Problem Solving Real World]

7. Megan has two $1 bills, 2 quarters, 1 dime, and 3 nickels. Does she have enough money to buy a snack that costs $2.99? Explain.

_____

Lesson Check

1. Which is the greater amount of money, 1 dollar, 3 nickels, and 1 penny or 6 quarters, 1 dime, and 3 pennies?

   _____

   _____

   _____

2. Hannah wants to buy a kite for $4.75. She has 3 dollar bills, 7 quarters, and 1 dime. Does she have enough money to buy the kite? Explain.

   _____

   _____

   _____

Spiral Review

3. What time is shown on the clock?

   Ⓐ 2:42

   Ⓑ 3:42

   Ⓒ 8:12

   Ⓓ 9:12

4. Airplanes can travel at speeds of about 600 miles per hour. Trains can travel at speeds of about 150 miles per hour. How much faster can airplanes travel than trains?

   Ⓐ 750 miles per hour

   Ⓑ 615 miles per hour

   Ⓒ 450 miles per hour

   Ⓓ 425 miles per hour

5. About how long is your color marker?

   Ⓐ 6 centimeters

   Ⓑ 6 inches

   Ⓒ 6 feet

   Ⓓ 6 meters

6. Shawn has 359 baseball cards. Midori has 116 baseball cards. How many more baseball cards does Shawn have?

   Ⓐ 243

   Ⓑ 263

   Ⓒ 465

   Ⓓ 475

Name _____

Make Change

Essential Question How can you make change from $5.00 or less by counting on?

Unlock the Problem (Real World)

Justin buys a leash for his dog for $3.59. He pays with a $5 bill. How much change should he get?

Change is the money you get back if you have paid for an item with coins or bills that have a value greater than the cost of the item.

- • What is the cost of the leash?
  _____
- • What is the amount paid?
  _____
- • Why does Justin get change?
  _____

Activity 1 Make change from $5.00.

Materials ■ play money

STEP 1 Start with the cost of the item. Count on coins and bills to $5.00.

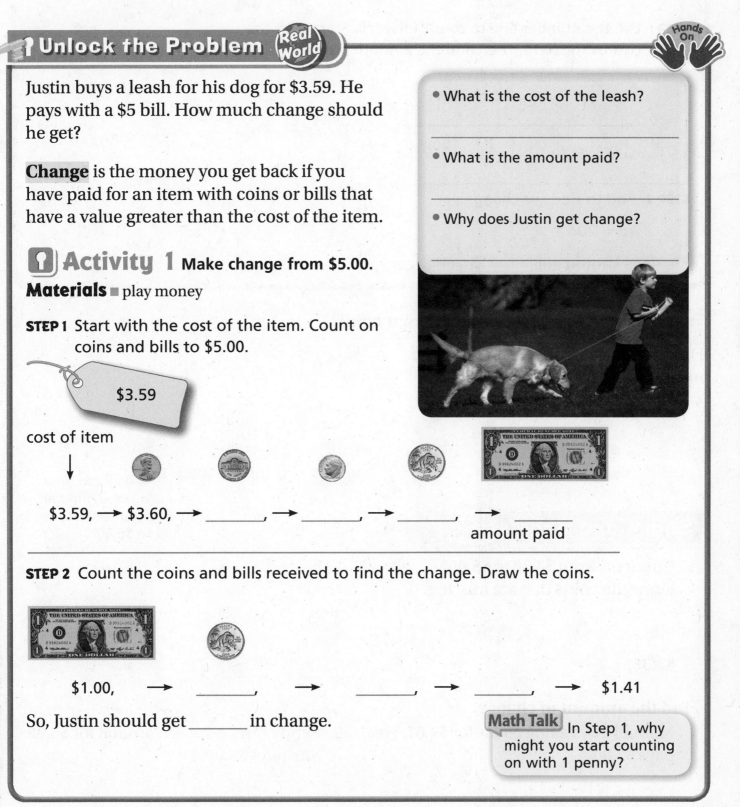

$3.59

cost of item

$3.59, → $3.60, → _____, → _____, → _____, → _____

amount paid

STEP 2 Count the coins and bills received to find the change. Draw the coins.

$1.00, → _____, → _____, → _____, → $1.41

So, Justin should get _____ in change.

Math Talk In Step 1, why might you start counting on with 1 penny?

🔑 Activity 2 Make change from $2.00.

Rose buys a cat toy for $1.76. She pays $2.00.
What change should Rose get?

STEP 1 Use the number line to count forward. Start with the cost of the item. Then add the amount paid.

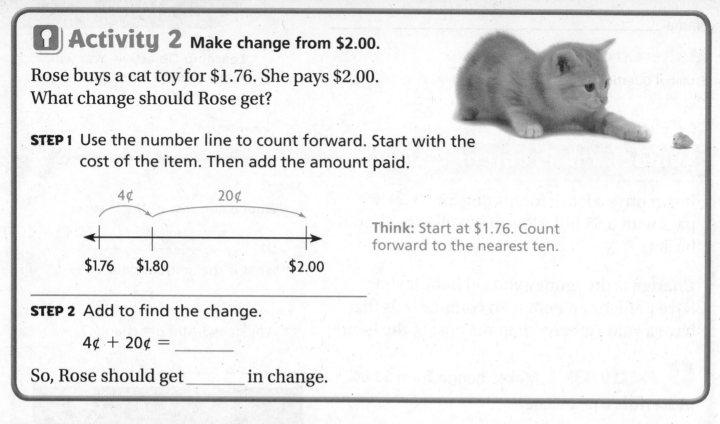

Think: Start at $1.76. Count forward to the nearest ten.

STEP 2 Add to find the change.

4¢ + 20¢ = _____

So, Rose should get _____ in change.

Try This! Make change using different coins.

Draw coins to show a different way to
make change from $2.00.

Math Talk Explain how you can use a number line to count on from $4.38 to $5.00.

Share and Show MATH BOARD

1. Count on from $4.38 to $5.00.
   Draw the coins that are missing.

   $4.38, _____, _____, _____, _____, _____,

Find the amount of change.

✓ 2. Manuel buys a dog collar for $1.67. He pays $2.00.

_____

✓ 3. Sandy buys a stuffed animal for $3.22. She pays $5.00.

_____

On Your Own

Find the amount of change.

4. Ben buys a carton of milk for $1.18. He pays $2.00.

_____

5. Kelly buys a book for $3.09. She pays with a $5 bill.

_____

6. Isaac buys a package of bird seed for $4.25. He pays $5.00.

_____

7. Eva buys a key chain for $2.76. She pays with three $1 bills.

_____

8. **Algebra** Complete the table.

Quarters	1	2	3	4	5	6	7	8
Value	$0.25	$0.50					$1.75	

Problem Solving • Applications (Real World)

9. **GO DEEPER** Melissa bought dog treats. She paid with a $5 bill. She got 2 quarters, 2 dimes, and 3 pennies in change. How much did the dog treats cost?

_____

Use the pictures for 10–12.

10. Vijay buys a can of tennis balls. He pays with a $5 bill. How much change should he receive?

_____

11. Sigrid buys swim goggles. She pays with four $1 bills and 4 quarters. How much change should she receive?

_____

12. Trevor bought a baseball cap. His change was $1 and 1 penny. How much money did Trevor give the cashier?

_____

13. **GO DEEPER** Karen buys a jump rope for $3.33. She pays with a $5 bill. How much is Karen's change? What bills and coins could she get? Explain your answer.

_____

_____

_____

_____

14. **THINK SMARTER** Sean buys lunch for $4.27. He pays with a $5 bill. How much change should Sean receive?

Ⓐ $0.73

Ⓑ $0.75

Ⓒ $0.81

Ⓓ $0.83

Connect to Social Studies

National Parks

In 2010, the U.S. Mint began releasing quarters with national parks and other national sites appearing on the reverse side (tails). Five such America the Beautiful Quarters® will be released each year through 2021. A national site from each state will be featured. The table shows the five national sites on 2017 quarters.

Ozark National Scenic Riverways

15. If you collect one of each of the America the Beautiful Quarters® designs for 2017, how much money

will you have? _____

16. Violet paid for a park map with a $5 bill. She got 8 quarters in change. How much was the park

map? _____

17. Tim has 6 quarters. He wants to buy a park decal for $3.00. Does Tim have enough money to buy the decal? Explain.

_____

2017 America the Beautiful Quarters®

National Site	State
Effigy Mounds National Monument	Iowa
Frederick Douglass National Historic Site	Washington, DC
Ozark National Scenic Riverways	Missouri
Ellis Island (Statue of Liberty National Monument)	New Jersey
George Rogers Clark National Historical Park	Indiana

Make change

Learning Objective You will make change from $5.00 or less by counting on.

Find the amount of change.

1. Riley buys a notepad for $1.59. She pays $2.00.

   _____ $0.41 _____

2. Mario buys a bag of peanuts for $3.45. He pays with a $5 bill.

   _____

3. Zach buys a comic book for $3.00. He pays with three $1 bills.

   _____

4. Liam buys a bottle of water for $1.55. He pays $2.00.

   _____

5. Latrell buys an action figure for $4.39. He pays $5.00.

   _____

6. Lu Chen buys a pack of cards for $3.00. She pays with a $5 bill.

   _____

Use the pictures for 7–8.

Juice $1.39 $2.74   POP CORN $3.30

7. Sonya buys a bag of popcorn. She pays with three $1 bills and 2 quarters. How much change should Sonya receive?

   _____

8. Keesha buys a sandwich. Her change is 1 quarter and 1 penny. How much money did Keesha give the cashier?

   _____

9. **WRITE** ▸ *Math* Explain how to make change from $5.00 for an item that costs $3.18.

   _____

   _____

Lesson Check

1. Alicia buys a baseball for $4.27. She pays with a $5 bill. How much change should Alicia receive? Explain.

_____

_____

_____

2. Explain two different ways to make change for $2.00, when the cost is $1.64.

_____

_____

_____

_____

Spiral Review

3. What time is 3 hours 25 minutes after 4:30 P.M.?

Ⓐ 1:05 P.M.   Ⓒ 7:55 P.M.

Ⓑ 4:55 P.M.   Ⓓ 8:05 P.M.

4. Multiply.

$$\begin{array}{r} 52 \\ \times\ 5 \\ \hline \end{array}$$

Ⓐ 2,510

Ⓑ 260

Ⓒ 57

Ⓓ 47

5. Moira has 247 pennies in a jar. Latifa has 168 pennies. How many pennies do the two girls have in all?

Ⓐ 415

Ⓑ 405

Ⓒ 315

Ⓓ 305

6. Ricardo has 2 quarters, 4 dimes, and 2 nickels. Which amount of money is greater than Ricardo's amount?

Ⓐ 2 dimes, 5 nickels

Ⓑ 3 quarters, 1 penny

Ⓒ 4 quarters, 1 penny

Ⓓ 9 dimes, 7 pennies

Name _____

Equivalent Periods of Time

Essential Question How can you use what you know about equivalent periods of time to solve problems?

Learning Objective You will use models to identify and solve problems related to equivalent periods of time.

 **Unlock the Problem** Real World

The analog clock below has an hour hand, a minute hand, and a **second** hand to measure time. The time is 4:30:12.

Read Math

Read 4:30:12 as 4:30 and 12 seconds, or 30 minutes and 12 seconds after 4.

- Are there more minutes or seconds in one hour?

_____

There are 60 seconds in a minute and 60 minutes in an hour. The clocks show how far the hands move for each length of time.

Start Time: 3:00:00

1 second elapses.

The time is now 3:00:01.

1 minute, or 60 seconds, elapses. The second hand has made a full turn clockwise.

The time is now 3:01:00.

1 hour, or 60 minutes, elapses. The minute hand has made a full turn clockwise.

The time is now 4:00:00.

🔑 Example 1 How many minutes are in 4 hours?

There are _____ minutes in 1 hour.

_____ × 60 minutes = _____ minutes

So, there are _____ minutes in 4 hours.

Think: Multiply the number of minutes in an hour by the number of hours.

 **Math Talk**

Math Processes and Practices ❶

Analyze How many full turns clockwise does a minute hand make in 4 hours? Explain.

🔒 Example 2 Compare measures.

Quinn spent 2 hours on her science project.
Chad spent 200 minutes on his science project.
Who spent more time?

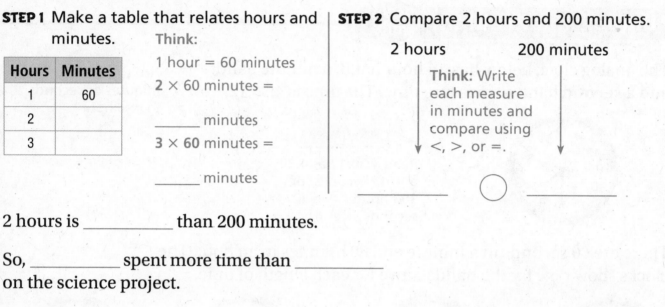

STEP 1 Make a table that relates hours and minutes.

Hours	Minutes
1	60
2	
3	

Think:

1 hour = 60 minutes

2 × 60 minutes =

_____ minutes

3 × 60 minutes =

_____ minutes

STEP 2 Compare 2 hours and 200 minutes.

2 hours   200 minutes

Think: Write each measure in minutes and compare using <, >, or =.

_____ ◯ _____

2 hours is _____ than 200 minutes.

So, _____ spent more time than _____
on the science project.

🔒 Activity Compare the length of a week to the length of a day.

Materials ■ color pencils

The number line below shows the relationship between days and weeks.

STEP 1 Use a color pencil to shade 1 week on the number line.

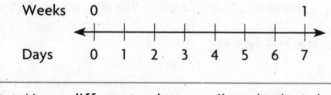

Weeks   0   1

Days   0   1   2   3   4   5   6   7

STEP 2 Use a different color pencil to shade 1 day on the number line.

STEP 3 Compare the size of 1 week to the size of 1 day.

There are _____ days in _____ week.

So, 1 week is _____ times 1 day.

Equivalent Units of Time
There are 24 hours in 1 day.
There are 7 days in 1 week.
There are about 4 weeks in 1 month.
There are 12 months in 1 year.
There are about 52 weeks in 1 year.
There are about 365 days in 1 year.
There are about 30 days in 1 month.

Math Talk

Math Processes and Practices ❷

Represent a Problem Explain how you can make a table to find the number of days in 5 weeks.

Name _____

1. Compare the length of a year to the length of a month. Use a model to help.

Years   0   1

Months   0   1   2   3   4   5   6   7   8   9   10   11   12

1 year is _____ times _____ month.

Equivalent Units of Time
1 minute = 60 seconds
1 hour = 60 minutes
1 day = 24 hours
1 week = 7 days
1 month = 28, 29, 30, or 31 days
1 year = 12 months
1 year is about 52 weeks

Complete.

✓ 2. 2 minutes = _____ seconds

✓ 3. 4 years = _____ months

Math Talk   Math Processes and Practices ④

Use Models Explain how the number line helped you compare the length of a year to the length of a month.

Complete.

4. 3 minutes = _____ seconds

5. 4 hours = _____ minutes

6. 5 weeks = _____ days

Math Processes and Practices ④ **Use Symbols** **Algebra** Compare using <, >, or =.

7. 3 years ◯ 35 months

8. 2 days ◯ 40 hours

9. 3 months ◯ 90 days
Think: 1 month is about 30 days.

10. **GO DEEPER** Dylan has lived in the apartment building for 5 years. Kyle has lived there for 250 weeks. Who has lived in the building longer? Explain. Complete the table to help.

_____

_____

Years	Weeks
1	
2	
3	
4	
5	

11. **THINK SMARTER** Kylie was on vacation with her family for 3 weeks. Her friend Jenna was on vacation for 19 days. Who was on vacation for a longer period of time? Explain.

_____

_____

12. **Math Processes and Practices ⑤ Communicate** Explain how you know that 115 hours is less than 5 days.

_____

_____

13. **THINK SMARTER**   Draw lines to match equivalent units of time. Some units might not have a match.

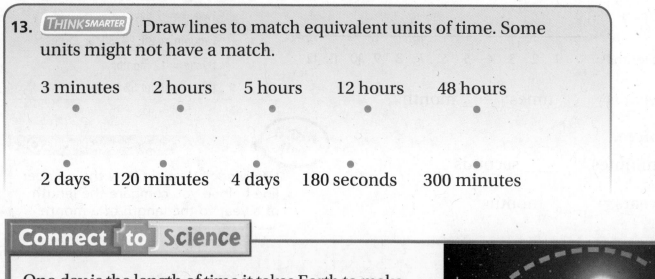

3 minutes   2 hours   5 hours   12 hours   48 hours
   •   •   •   •   •

   •   •   •   •   •
2 days   120 minutes   4 days   180 seconds   300 minutes

Connect to Science

One day is the length of time it takes Earth to make one complete rotation. One year is the time it takes Earth to revolve around the sun. To make the calendar match Earth's orbit time, there are leap years. Leap years add one extra day to the year. A leap day, February 29, is added to the calendar every four years.

> 1 year = 365 days
> 1 leap year = 366 days

14. How many days are there in 4 years, if the fourth year is a leap year? Explain. Complete the table to help.

Years	Days
1	
2	
3	
4	

_____

15. Parker was born on February 29, 2008. The second time he is able to celebrate on his actual birthday is in 2016. How many days old was Parker on February 29, 2016? Explain your answer.

_____

Equivalent Periods of Time

Learning Objective You will use models to identify and solve problems related to equivalent periods of time.

Complete.

1. 2 months is about _____60_____ days

   Think: 1 month is about 30 days,
   so 2 months is 2 × 30 days, or 60 days

2. 4 weeks = _____ days

3. 3 years is about _____ weeks

4. 2 hours = _____ minutes

5. 4 minutes = _____ seconds

Compare using <, >, or =.

6. 2 years ◯ 14 months

7. 3 hours ◯ 300 minutes

8. 5 days ◯ 120 hours

9. 4 years ◯ 200 weeks

Problem Solving Real World

10. Caleb practiced a piano piece for 300 seconds. Delia practiced a piano piece for 5 minutes. Who practiced longer? Explain.

   _____

   _____

   _____

11. Carly's younger brother just turned 3 years old. Tony's brother is now 30 months old. Whose brother is older? Explain.

   _____

   _____

   _____

12. **WRITE** ▸ Math Explain why 3 weeks is less than 24 days.

   _____

   _____

Lesson Check

1. Josh rode his bike for 2 hours. For how many minutes did he ride his bike?

2. Thalia's vacation lasts exactly 4 weeks. Peter is taking the month of July as vacation. Whose vacation lasts longer?

Spiral Review

3. Kayla bought $\frac{9}{4}$ pounds of apples. What is that weight written as a mixed number?

4. Brett buys breakfast for $4.28. He pays with a $5 bill. How much change does Brett get?

5. Marcy rode her bike $\frac{7}{10}$ mile to the tennis courts. Then she rode another $\frac{2}{10}$ mile to the park. How far did Marcy ride in all?

6. Arturo rode his scooter $\frac{3}{10}$ mile. Jen rode her scooter $\frac{3}{4}$ mile. Who rode the lesser distance?

Name _____

Measure and Use Time Intervals

Essential Question How can you measure and use elapsed time to solve problems?

Learning Objective You will use clocks and number lines as strategies to solve elapsed time problems.

🔑 Unlock the Problem (Real World)

Jared and his family are planning a walking tour of Colonial Williamsburg. Their tour starts at 2:00 P.M. and ends at 4:00 P.M. How long does the tour last?

Elapsed time is the amount of time that passes from the start of an activity to the end of the activity.

🔒 One Way Use a clock to find elapsed time.

STEP 1 Find the starting time on the clock.

_____

STEP 2 Count the hours by counting on by ones to 4:00 P.M.

From 2:00 to 4:00 is _____ hours.

So, the elapsed time is _____ hours.

🔒 Another Way Use subtraction to find elapsed time.

STEP 1 Write the ending time. Then write the starting time so that the hours and minutes line up.

_____

STEP 2 The minutes are the same, so subtract the hours.

So, the elapsed time is _____ hours.

The tour lasts _____ hours.

```
     :00  → end time
  −  :00  → start time
  _____
     :00  → elapsed time
```

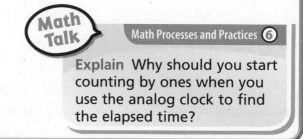

Math Talk — Math Processes and Practices ⑥

Explain Why should you start counting by ones when you use the analog clock to find the elapsed time?

Find Ending and Starting Times.

🔑 Examples

Sophie meets her friends at Virginia Beach at 12:00 noon. She spends 5 hours paddleboarding and swimming. At what time does Sophie leave the beach?

Ⓐ Use a clock to find the ending time.

STEP 1 Find the starting time on the clock.

_____

STEP 2 Count forward by ones for the elapsed time of 5 hours. Write the missing counting numbers next to the clock.

So, the ending time is _____

_____

Raven's 4th-grade class took a bus on a field trip to Richmond. The trip lasted 4 hours. The bus returned to school at 4:30 P.M. At what time did the bus leave the school?

Ⓑ Use a number line to find the starting time.

STEP 1 Find the time on the number line when the bus returned to school.

_____

STEP 2 Count back on the number line to subtract the elapsed time. Draw and label the jumps to show the hours.

_____

STEP 3 Write the times below the number line.

4:30 P.M.

You jumped back to _____

So, the bus left the school at _____

Name _____

1. Use the clock to find the elapsed time if the starting time is 1:00 P.M. and the ending time is 5:00 P.M.

_____ hours

Find the starting or ending time.

2. Starting time: 1:30 P.M.
   Elapsed time: 6 hours

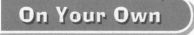
1:30 P.M.

_____

3. Ending time: 11:00 A.M.
   Elapsed time: 3 hours

Math Talk   Math Processes and Practices ②

Use Reasoning How do you find the starting time when you know the ending time and the elapsed time?

4. Find the elapsed time.

Starting time: 4:30 A.M.   Ending time: 10:30 A.M.

_____ hours

10: ▢
− ▢:30
___
▢:▢

Find the ending or starting time.

5. Ending time: 11:30 P.M.
   Elapsed time: 5 hours

← ─────────┼→
          11:30 P.M.

_____

6. Starting time: 3:00 A.M.
   Elapsed time: 4 hours

_____

Problem Solving • Applications (Real World)

7. Tyrone went on a beach bike tour of Virginia Beach. He left at 9:30 A.M. and returned at 11:30 A.M. How long did the bike tour last?

_____

8. Pose a Problem Write and solve a problem similar to Problem 7. Exchange the known and the unknown information.

_____

_____

_____

9. THINK SMARTER Tracy began fishing at 5:30 A.M. and fished until 10:30 A.M. Ethan finished fishing at 11:00 A.M. He fished for the same length of time as Tracy. At what time did Ethan start fishing? **Explain.**

_____

_____

10. GO DEEPER Jade starts cleaning her room at 5:30 P.M. and finishes at 6:30 P.M. Her sister Hope finishes cleaning her room at 7:00 P.M. She cleans for the same amount of time as Jade. At what time does Hope start cleaning?

_____

11. THINK SMARTER Chloe's paddleboard lesson began at 2:30 P.M. Her lesson lasted 2 hours. Draw hands on the clock to show the time Chloe's paddleboard lesson ended.

Measure and Use Time Intervals

Learning Objective You will use clocks and number lines as strategies to solve elapsed time problems.

Find the elapsed time.

1. Starting time: 4:30 P.M.
   Ending time: 7:30 P.M.

   ```
     7 : 30    end time
   – 4 : 30    start time
     3 : 00    elapsed time
   ```

   _____
   3 hours
   _____

2. Starting time: 10:00 A.M.
   Ending time: 12:00 noon

   _____

Find the starting or ending time.

3. Starting time: 3:00 P.M.
   Elapsed time: 5 hours

   ⟵————————————————⟶
   3:00 P.M.

   _____

4. Ending time: 11:30 A.M.
   Elapsed time: 9 hours

   _____

Problem Solving (Real World)

5. Heather spent 2 hours doing research on the Internet. She finished at 7:30 P.M. At what time did Heather start her research?

   _____

6. Cyrus left for camp at 8:00 A.M. He arrived 3 hours later. At what time did Cyrus arrive at camp?

   _____

7. **WRITE** ▸*Math* Describe a situation in your life when you need to know how to find a starting time.

   _____

   _____

Lesson Check

1. Cody and his friends started playing a game at 6:30 P.M. It took them 2 hours to finish the game. At what time did they finish?

_____

2. Delia worked for 3 hours on her oil painting. She finished at 11:30 A.M. At what time did Delia start working on the painting?

_____

Spiral Review

3. Georgie has four $1 bills, 2 quarters, 1 dime, 3 nickels, and 4 pennies. How much money does Georgie have?

_____

4. Jose worked on the class science project for 3 weeks. Daniella worked on the science project for 23 days. Who worked on the science project a longer period of time?

_____

5. There are 16 pieces of color chalk in a box. How many pieces of chalk are in 4 boxes?

_____

6. Belle wrote this number pattern. 32, 46, 19, 32, 46, 19, 32, 46, 19, 32 What is the pattern core? What is the next number in the pattern?

_____

138

Name _____

Estimate and Measure Customary and Metric Length

Learning Objective You will estimate and measure length using customary and metric units.

Essential Question How can you estimate and measure length using customary and metric units?

🔑 Unlock the Problem · Real World

You can estimate and measure length and distance to the nearest half inch, **inch**, **foot**, and **yard** using customary units.

A marker is about half inch wide.	A small paper clip is about 1 inch long.	A piece of paper is about 1 foot long.	A baseball bat is about 1 yard long.
Name an object that is about half inch wide.	**Name an object that is about 1 inch long.**	**Name an object that is about 1 foot long.**	**Name an object that is about 1 yard long.**

You can estimate and measure length and distance to the nearest **centimeter** and **meter** using metric units.

A child's finger is about 1 centimeter wide.	**Name an object that is about 1 centimeter wide.** _____
A door is about 1 meter wide.	**Name an object that is about 1 meter wide.** _____

Math Talk Name an object in your classroom that you would measure in yards. Why wouldn't you measure this object in inches?

🔒 Activity 1 Materials ■ inch ruler ■ centimeter ruler

Think: Measuring to the nearest half inch and centimeter is like rounding a number.

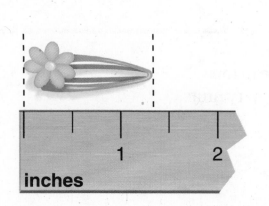

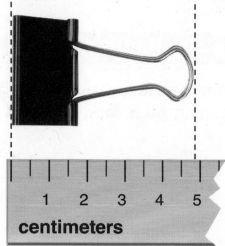

- Line up the left end of the hair clip with the zero mark on the ruler.

- The right end of the hair clip is between the half-inch marks for

  _____ and _____.

The length of the hair clip is closer to

_____ inches than to _____ inch.
So, the length of the hair clip to the

nearest half inch is _____ inches.

- Line up the left end of the clip with the zero mark on the ruler.

- The right end of the clip is between the centimeter marks for

  _____ and _____.

The length of the clip is closer to _____

centimeters than to _____ centimeters.
So, the length of the clip to the nearest

centimeter is _____ centimeters.

🔒 Activity 2

Materials ■ inch ruler ■ centimeter ruler
■ yardstick ■ meter stick

Think: Half inch, inch, and centimeter are for shorter lengths. Foot, yard, and meter are for longer lengths and distances.

STEP 1 Choose objects or distances to measure. Estimate the length of each object or distance. Record your estimates in the table.

Length of Objects			
Object	**Estimate**	**Unit**	**Measure**
		half inch	
		inch	
		centimeter	
		foot	
		yard	
		meter	

STEP 2 Measure each object or distance with the correct unit of measure. Record your measurements in the table.

Math Talk What strategy did you use to find your estimate?

Name _____

1. To the nearest half inch, how long is this crayon? _____

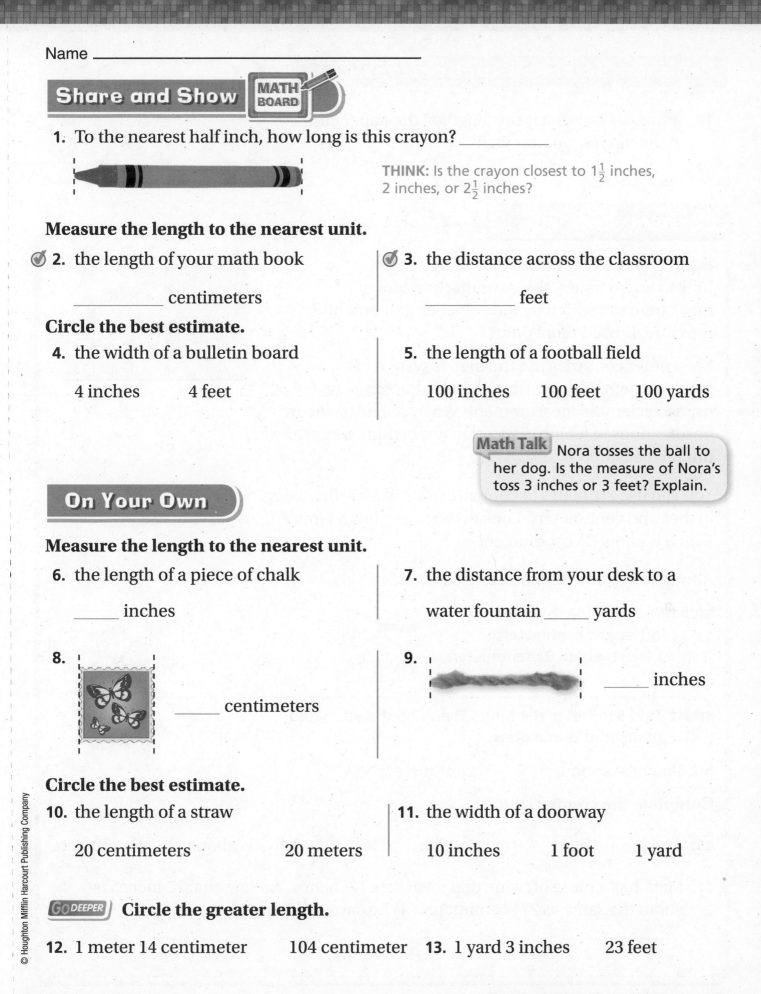

THINK: Is the crayon closest to $1\frac{1}{2}$ inches, 2 inches, or $2\frac{1}{2}$ inches?

Measure the length to the nearest unit.

2. the length of your math book

_____ centimeters

3. the distance across the classroom

_____ feet

Circle the best estimate.

4. the width of a bulletin board

4 inches   4 feet

5. the length of a football field

100 inches   100 feet   100 yards

Math Talk Nora tosses the ball to her dog. Is the measure of Nora's toss 3 inches or 3 feet? Explain.

On Your Own

Measure the length to the nearest unit.

6. the length of a piece of chalk

_____ inches

7. the distance from your desk to a water fountain _____ yards

8.

_____ centimeters

9.

_____ inches

Circle the best estimate.

10. the length of a straw

20 centimeters   20 meters

11. the width of a doorway

10 inches   1 foot   1 yard

GO DEEPER Circle the greater length.

12. 1 meter 14 centimeter   104 centimeter

13. 1 yard 3 inches   23 feet

© Houghton Mifflin Harcourt Publishing Company

Problem Solving · Applications (Real World)

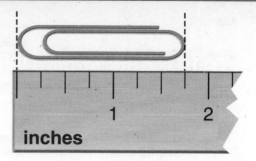

14. (THINK SMARTER) What is the length of the paper clip to the nearest quarter inch?

_____

Connect to Science

Inches and Centimeters

In the United States, the customary system of measurement, which includes inches as a unit of measure, is used more often.

Most other countries use the metric system of measurement. The metric system is almost always used in scientific measurement. When scientists record observations of length, they often use centimeters as the unit of measure.

You can use estimates to compare units of measure using inches and centimeters. Look at the ruler above. Notice that 1 inch is about $2\frac{1}{2}$ centimeters.

About how many centimeters is 5 inches?

STEP 1 Make a table to compare inches and centimeters.
1 inch is about $2\frac{1}{2}$ centimeters.

Inches	1	2	3	4	5	6
Centimeters	$2\frac{1}{2}$	5	$7\frac{1}{2}$	10	$12\frac{1}{2}$	15

STEP 2 Find 5 inches in the table. Then find the estimated number of centimeters.

So, 5 inches is about _____ centimeters.

Complete the comparison.

15. 4 inches is about _____ centimeters.   **16.**   10 inches is about _____ centimeters.

17. Mark has a piece of twine that measures 12 inches. He says that 12 inches is about the same as $27\frac{1}{2}$ centimeters. Is he correct? Explain.

_____

_____

Name _____

Estimate and Measure Customary and Metric Length

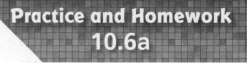
Learning Objective You will estimate and measure length using customary and metric units.

Measure the length to the nearest unit.

1. _2_ centimeters

2. _____ inches

Circle the best estimate.

3. length of eyeglasses

   12 centimeters   12 meters

4. height of an adult

   6 inches   6 feet   6 yards

5. distance to the school library

   16 centimeters   16 meters

6. width of a soccer field

   80 inches   80 feet   80 yards

Problem Solving Real World

7. Luis is using a ruler to measure the length of a marker. He says that the length is $5\frac{1}{2}$ inches. Is he correct? Explain how you know.

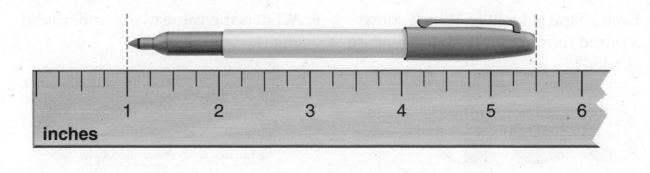

_____

_____

8. **WRITE** ▸Math Write a problem about choosing a customary unit of measure to solve a problem.

_____

_____

Lesson Check

1. About how long is your pencil?

(A) 16 inches

(B) 6 feet

(C) 16 centimeters

(D) 16 meters

2. What unit of measure would you use to measure the length of a piece of spaghetti?

(A) inch

(B) hour

(C) yard

(D) meter

Spiral Review

3. Which shows the numbers in order from least to greatest?

(A) 9,684; 9,683; 9,682; 9,681

(B) 9,681; 9,682; 9,683; 9,684

(C) 9,680; 9,683; 9,682; 9,681

(D) 9,684; 9,638; 9,628; 9,680

4. Which number comes next in the pattern? 358, 354, 350, 346, ■

(A) 350

(B) 342

(C) 341

(D) 332

5. Each shape is 1 whole. Which shows a mixed number for the parts that are shaded?

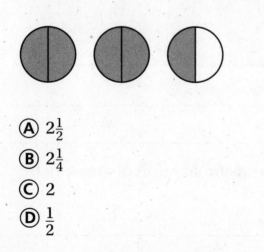

(A) $2\frac{1}{2}$

(B) $2\frac{1}{4}$

(C) 2

(D) $\frac{1}{2}$

6. What is the value of the underlined digit?

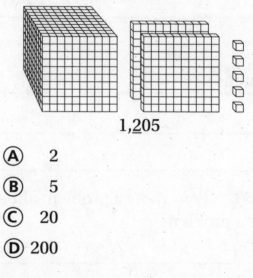

1,<u>2</u>05

(A) 2

(B) 5

(C) 20

(D) 200

Name _____

Estimate and Measure Customary Liquid Volume

Essential Question How can you estimate and measure liquid volume in customary units?

Learning Objective You will estimate and measure liquid volume in cups, pints, quarts, and gallons.

🔑 Unlock the Problem

Some common customary units used to measure liquid volume are **cup (c)**, **pint (pt)**, **quart (qt)**, and **gallon (gal)**.

| 1 cup (c) | 1 pint (pt) | 1 quart (qt) | 1 gallon (gal) |

🔓 Activity

Materials ■ cup, pint, quart, and gallon containers; water

Number of Cups		
Number of Cups in a Pint	Number of Cups in a Quart	Number of Cups in a Gallon
Estimate			
Capacity			

STEP 1 Estimate the number of cups it will take to fill the pint container. Record your estimate.

STEP 2 Fill a cup and pour it into the pint container. Repeat until the pint container is full. Record the number of cups it took to fill the pint container.

STEP 3 Repeat Steps 1–2 for the quart and gallon containers.

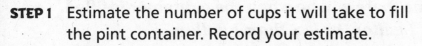

Math Talk

Math Processes and Practices ②

Reason Abstractly What amount might you measure with a cup? Explain.

1. How do your measurements compare to your estimates?

_____

2. Which unit would you use to measure the amount of water needed to fill an aquarium? **Explain.**

_____

① Example Solve a problem about liquid volume.

Dan drinks 8 cups of water each day. A bottle holds
2 cups of water. How many bottles of water does
Dan drink each day?

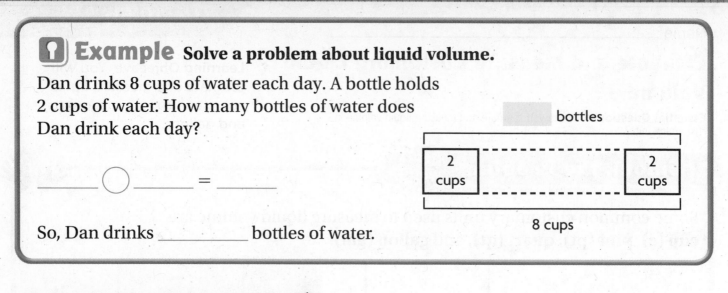

_____ bottles

| 2 cups | - - - - - - - - - | 2 cups |

8 cups

_____ ◯ _____ = _____

So, Dan drinks _____ bottles of water.

Share and Show MATH BOARD

**Choose the unit you would use to measure the liquid volume.
Write *cup*, *pint*, *quart*, or *gallon*.**

1.

Think: A cup is small.

_____

2.

_____

3.

_____

✓ 4.

_____

**Estimate how much liquid volume there will be when the container is filled.
Write *more than 1 gallon*, *about 1 gallon*, or *less than 1 gallon*.**

5.

_____

6.

_____

✓ 7.

_____

Math Talk

Math Processes and Practices ⑥

Explain how you estimate
the liquid volume of a
full container.

Name _____

Choose the unit you would use to measure the liquid volume.
Write *cup, pint, quart,* or *gallon.*

8.  9. 10. 11.

_____ _____ _____ _____

Estimate how much liquid volume there will be when the container is filled.
Write *more than 1 cup, about 1 cup,* or *less than 1 cup.*

12.  13.  14.

_____ _____ _____

15. Kacie buys 7 bottles of liquid dish soap. There are 2 pints of
soap in each bottle. How many pints of liquid dish soap does
Kacie buy?

_____

16. **WRITE** ▸*Math* Chris is bringing a bottle of water on an
afternoon hike. What size container should he bring?
Explain.

_____

17. Cody has a recipe for lime punch. He needs 4 quarts of club
soda. The store sells club soda in 2-quart bottles. How many
bottles does Cody need to buy?

_____

18. **GO DEEPER** Jocelyn brings 3 water jugs to her team's soccer
game. Christy brings another 4 water jugs. Each jug holds
2 gallons of water. How many gallons of water do the girls
bring to their soccer game?

_____

Problem Solving · Applications (Real World)

19. Janet is serving lemonade. Each glass holds 2 cups of lemonade. If Janet fills 9 glasses, how many cups of lemonade will she serve?

_____

20. **What's the Error?** Louis says his small water bottle can hold 3 quarts of water. Is he correct? **Explain.**

_____

_____

WRITE ▸ *Math* · **Show Your Work**

21. Connor's kitchen sink holds 8 gallons of water. He fills his sink with 2 gallons of water. How many more gallons of water can his kitchen sink hold?

_____

22. Sonia's punch bowl holds 5 pints of punch. She serves 2 pints of punch. How many pints are left in the punch bowl?

_____

23. **GO DEEPER** Amy drinks 8 cups of water every day. Troy drinks 6 cups of water every day. In five days, how many more cups of water does Amy drink than Troy?

_____

24. **THINK SMARTER** For 24a–24e, choose Yes or No to tell whether there will be more than one gallon of liquid when the container is filled.

   24a. travel mug   ○ Yes   ○ No

   24b. bathtub   ○ Yes   ○ No

   24c. spray bottle   ○ Yes   ○ No

   24d. small pitcher   ○ Yes   ○ No

   24e. swimming pool   ○ Yes   ○ No

Estimate and Measure Customary Liquid Volume

Learning Objective You will estimate and measure liquid volume in cups, pints, quarts, and gallons.

**Choose the unit you would use to measure the liquid volume.
Write *cup*, *pint*, *quart*, or *gallon*.**

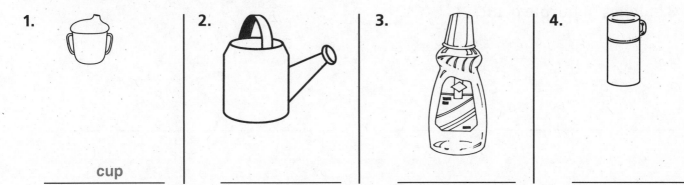

1. _____
   cup

2. _____

3. _____

4. _____

Estimate how much liquid volume there will be when the container is filled. Write *more than 1 gallon*, *about 1 gallon*, or *less than 1 gallon*.

5. _____

6. _____

7. _____

Problem Solving Real World

8. A lemonade recipe calls for 16 cups of water. Riley divides the recipe into two equal batches. How many cups of water are in each batch?

   _____

9. A basketball team fills a 5-gallon cooler with water. After a game, there are 2 gallons of water left in the cooler. How many gallons of water did the basketball team drink?

   _____

Lesson Check

1. A painter mixes 2 cups of red paint with blue paint to make a batch of purple paint. How many cups of red paint does the painter need to make 3 batches of purple paint?

2. A large pot can hold 16 pints of water. Peter fills the pot with 9 pints of water. How many more pints of water can the pot hold?

Spiral Review

3. The table shows the distance each student lives from school. Which student lives the *greatest* distance from school?

Distance from School	
Student	Distance
Deanna	$\frac{1}{2}$ mile
Lee-Ann	$\frac{3}{8}$ mile
Aaron	$\frac{4}{10}$ mile
Kareem	$\frac{5}{6}$ mile

Ⓐ Deanna   Ⓒ Aaron

Ⓑ Lee-Ann   Ⓓ Kareem

4. Which number sentence is in the same set of related facts as $24 \div 6 = 4$?

Ⓐ $3 \times 8 = 24$

Ⓑ $24 - 6 = 18$

Ⓒ $6 \times 4 = 24$

Ⓓ $24 - 4 = 20$

5. Marcus has 415 baseball cards. Jasmine has 187 baseball cards. How many more cards does Marcus have than Jasmine?

6. Mario puts 6 baseball cards on each page of an album. How many cards will he put on 5 pages?

Name _____

Temperature

Essential Question How do you estimate and measure temperature in degrees Fahrenheit and degrees Celsius?

Learning Objective You will estimate and measure temperature in degrees Fahrenheit and degrees Celsius.

🔑 Unlock the Problem (Real World)

Temperature is the measure of how hot or cold something is. **Degrees Fahrenheit (°F)** are customary units of temperature.

To read a thermometer, find the number closest to the top of the red bar. Use the scale along each side like a number line.

🔓 Activity 1

Materials ▪ Fahrenheit thermometer

STEP 1 Estimate what you think the outdoor temperature will be, in degrees Fahrenheit, three times during the day. Record your estimates.

STEP 2 Use a thermometer to measure the outdoor temperature at the times you chose. Record the actual temperature in degrees Fahrenheit.

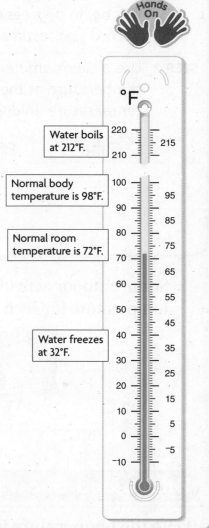

Water boils at 212°F.
Normal body temperature is 98°F.
Normal room temperature is 72°F.
Water freezes at 32°F.

Time	Estimate (°F)	Actual (°F)

1. How did each of the actual temperatures compare to normal room temperature?

_____

2. Some outdoor activities are shown below. Choose the better temperature for each activity.

20°F   75°F

32°F   90°F

Math Talk — Math Processes and Practices ③

Compare Representations How does knowing the normal room temperature help you estimate the outside temperature?

Degrees Celsius (°C) are metric units of temperature.

🔑 Activity 2

Materials ■ Celsius thermometer

STEP 1 Estimate what you think the outdoor temperature will be, in degrees Celsius, three times during the day. Record your estimates.

STEP 2 Use a thermometer to measure the outdoor temperature at the times you chose. Record the actual temperature. in degrees Celsius.

Time	Estimate (°C)	Actual (°C)

°C

— 130
120 — — 110
Water boils at 100°C. — 100 — 90
80 — — 70
60 — — 50
Normal body temperature is 37°C. — 40 — 30
Normal room temperature is 20°C. — 20 — 10
Water freezes at 0°C. — 0
— –10
–20 — –30
–40 —
— –50

3. Some outdoor activities are shown below. Choose the better temperature for each activity.

0°C   32°C

0°C   15°C

Share and Show 📐 MATH BOARD

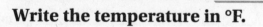

Write the temperature in °F.

1.

50 —
       — 45
40 —
       — 35
30 —

°F

_____

Think: The scale on a thermometer is like a number line. What number does the tick mark closest to the red bar represent?

✓ **2.**

20 —
       — 15
10 —
       — 5
0 —

°F

_____

3.

_____

Name _____

Write the temperature in °C.

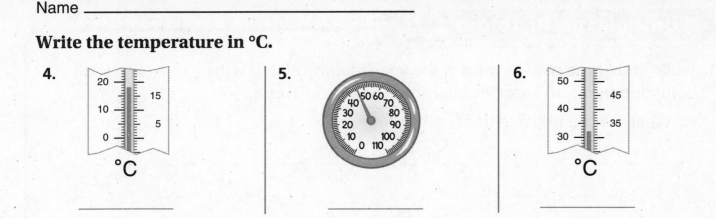

4.

°C

_____

5.

6.

°C

_____

Choose the better temperature for the activity.

7.

1°C   33°C

✓ 8.

75°F   42°F

Math Talk

Math Processes and Practices ②

Use Reasoning How do benchmark temperatures help you to solve Exercise 7?

On Your Own

9. It is 3°C outside. What is an activity that Brandon might do at this temperature? What clothes do you think he might wear?

_____

_____

_____

10. Lauren is wearing shorts and a pair of sandals. For 10a–10d, choose Yes or No to tell whether Lauren's clothing is reasonable for the outdoor temperature.

10a. 45°F   ◯ Yes   ◯ No

10b. 29°C   ◯ Yes   ◯ No

10c. 86°F   ◯ Yes   ◯ No

10d. 10°C   ◯ Yes   ◯ No

🔑 Unlock the Problem Real World

11. Joelle and Maria plan to swim at the beach today. Which is the better temperature for swimming at the beach, 53°F or 82°F?

a. What are you asked to find?

_____

_____

b. How would you describe the weather when it is 82°F outside?

_____

_____

c. How would you describe the weather when it is 53°F outside?

_____

_____

d. Which is the better temperature for swimming at the beach, 53°F or 82°F?

_____

_____

12. **GO DEEPER** **Sense or Nonsense?** Ari is snowboarding with his family. He says the temperature is 28°C. Is his statement sense or nonsense?

_____

_____

_____

13. **THINK SMARTER** Select the activities that can be done when the outdoor temperature is 77°F. Mark all that apply.

Ⓐ taking a boat ride

Ⓑ snowboarding

Ⓒ working in the garden

Ⓓ riding a bike

Ⓔ building a snow fort

Name _____

Temperature

Learning Objective You will estimate and measure temperature in degrees Fahrenheit and degrees Celsius.

Write the temperature in °F.

1.

°F

_78°F_

2.

°F

_____

3.

_____

Write the temperature in °C.

4.

_____

5.

°C

_____

6.

°C

_____

Choose the better temperature for the activity.

7.

5°C   21°C

8.

18°F   58°F

9.

80°F   30°F

Problem Solving Real World

10. Kara has a soccer game tonight. Which would be the better temperature for the game, 68°F or 8°F?

_____

11. It is 2°C. Describe an outdoor activity you might be doing and the clothes you might be wearing.

_____

_____

Lesson Check

1. A dog's normal body temperature is warmer than a human's normal body temperature. Is a dog's normal body temperature closer to 20°C or 38°C?

_____

2. Julia is reading a book outside. Which is the best estimate for the temperature outside?

Ⓐ 20°F

Ⓑ 40°F

Ⓒ 50°F

Ⓓ 70°F

Spiral Review

3. Alejandro's gymnastics class starts at 3:30 P.M. and lasts one hour. What time does his class end?

_____

3. Cory's family ate $\frac{5}{6}$ of a large pepperoni pizza and $\frac{1}{3}$ of a large cheese pizza. Which pizza had a smaller part left?

_____

5. Myra has two $1 bills, 1 quarter, 2 dimes, and 3 nickels. How much money does Myra have in all?

_____

6. Mr. Caruso buys a dozen eggs for $2.67. He pays with three $1 bills. How much change does he get?

_____

Name _____

Draw Plane Shapes

Essential Question How can you draw plane shapes using points, lines, line segments, and rays?

Learning Objective You will draw plane shapes using points, lines, line segments, and rays.

You have learned that a plane shape is a shape on a flat surface. Plane shapes are formed by connecting line segments at their endpoints.

Term and Definition	Draw It	Read It	Write It
A **point** is an exact location in space.	A •	point A	point A
A **line** is a straight path of points that continues without end in both directions.	B C	line BC line CB	$\overleftrightarrow{BC}$ $\overleftrightarrow{CB}$
A **line segment** is part of a line between two **endpoints**. Endpoints are used to show segments of lines.	D E	line segment DE line segment ED	$\overline{DE}$ $\overline{ED}$
A **ray** is a part of a line that has one endpoint and continues without end in one direction. A ray is always named by its endpoint first.	F G	ray FG	$\overrightarrow{FG}$

Activity Draw and label $\overline{JK}$.

Math Talk

Math Processes and Practices ⑥

Compare Explain how lines, line segments, and rays are related.

- Is there another way to name $\overline{JK}$? Explain.

_____

_____

🔒 Draw plane shapes.

Plane shapes have angles formed by the line segments that share endpoints, or vertices.

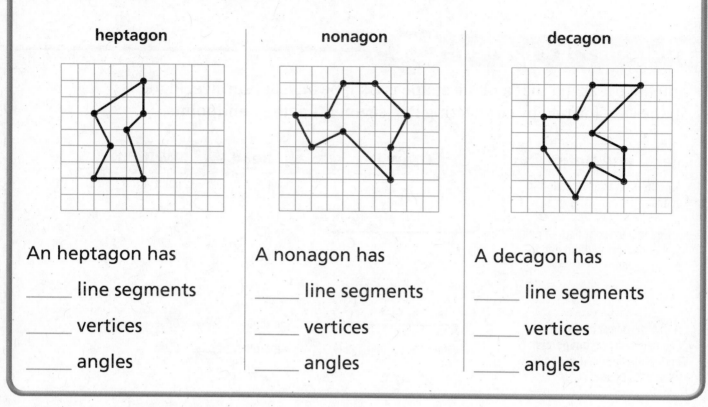

heptagon　　　　**nonagon**　　　　**decagon**

An heptagon has

_____ line segments

_____ vertices

_____ angles

A nonagon has

_____ line segments

_____ vertices

_____ angles

A decagon has

_____ line segments

_____ vertices

_____ angles

Try This! **Draw a plane shape.**

Draw a shape by connecting line segments at their endpoints. Use a ruler.

Name _____

Draw a shape that is described. Name the shape you drew. Use a ruler.

1. a shape with 3 angles

2. 5 line segments connected at their end points

3. 7 line segments connected at their end points

Draw and label an example of the shape.

4. $\overleftrightarrow{XY}$

5. point K

6. $\overrightarrow{CD}$

On Your Own

Draw a shape that is described. Name the shape you drew. Use a ruler.

7. a 4-sided shape with 4 right angles

8. 6 line segments connected at their end points

9. 8 line segments connected at their end points

Use Shape F for 10–11.

10. Name a line segment.

11. Name a point.

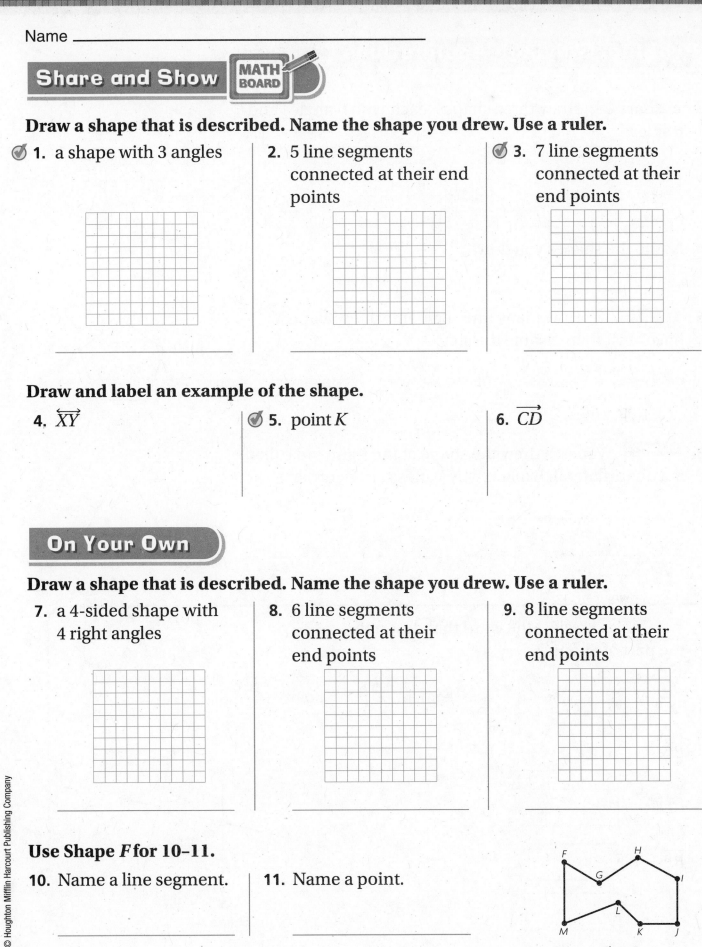

Shape F

© Houghton Mifflin Harcourt Publishing Company

Problem Solving • Applications (Real World)

13. **THINK SMARTER** Draw three shapes, each with 6 angles and 6 sides.

14. Name the shapes you drew.

_____

15. **THINK SMARTER** How many line segments does Shape X have? List them. Name the shape.

_____

_____

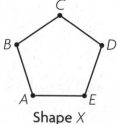

Shape X

16. **GO DEEPER** Vanessa drew the shape at the right and called it a quadrilateral. Explain why Vanessa is incorrect.

_____

_____

17. **THINK SMARTER** Select the word that describes the part of Shape A.

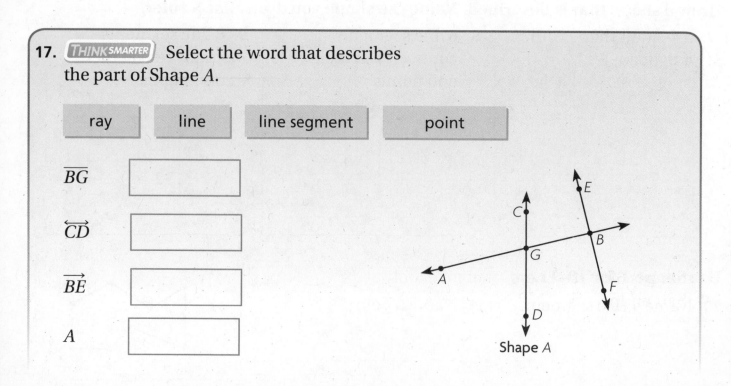

ray	line	line segment	point

$\overline{BG}$

$\overleftrightarrow{CD}$

$\overrightarrow{BE}$

A

Shape A

Draw Plane Shapes

Learning Objective You will draw points, line segments, and plane shapes, using a ruler or straightedge.

Draw a shape that is described. Name the shape you drew. Use a ruler.

1. $\overline{JK}$

Think: Another way to write $\overline{JK}$ is line segment JK.

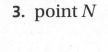

2. shape with 3 line segments and no right angles

3. point N

4. $\overline{BC}$

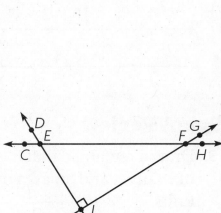

Use Shape S for 5 and 6.

5. Name a line segment.

6. Name a ray.

_____   _____

Shape S

Problem Solving Real World

7. In the polygon shown, line segment AC is comprised of which two line segments?

_____

_____

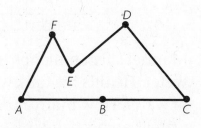

8. **WRITE** ▸*Math* Use a ruler to draw a shape that has 6 line segments that meet only at their endpoints.

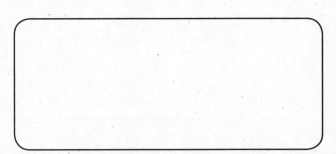

Lesson Check

1. What do you notice about the number of sides and the number of angles in the plane shape shown?

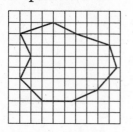

_____

_____

2. Milo wants to make a hexagon. He started to draw the shape and now needs help to finish it. Show a way to finish Milo's shape.

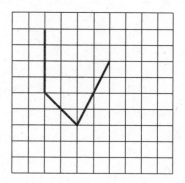

Spiral Review

3. Draw a rectangle that has a perimeter of 14 units and an area of 10 square units.

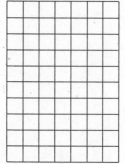

4. What fraction names the shaded part?

_____

5. Manuel's fish tank holds 9 gallons of water. He fills his tank with 5 gallons of water. How many more gallons of water can his fish tank hold?

_____

6. Carla has 40 small toys. She wants to put 5 toys in each gift bag for her party. How many gift bags can Carla make?

_____

Name _____

Classify Quadrilaterals

Essential Question How can you use sides and angles to help you describe quadrilaterals?

Learning Objective You will describe, classify, and compare quadrilaterals based on sides and angles.

🔑 Unlock the Problem (Real World)

Quadrilaterals are named by their sides and their angles.

🔑 **Describe quadrilaterals.**

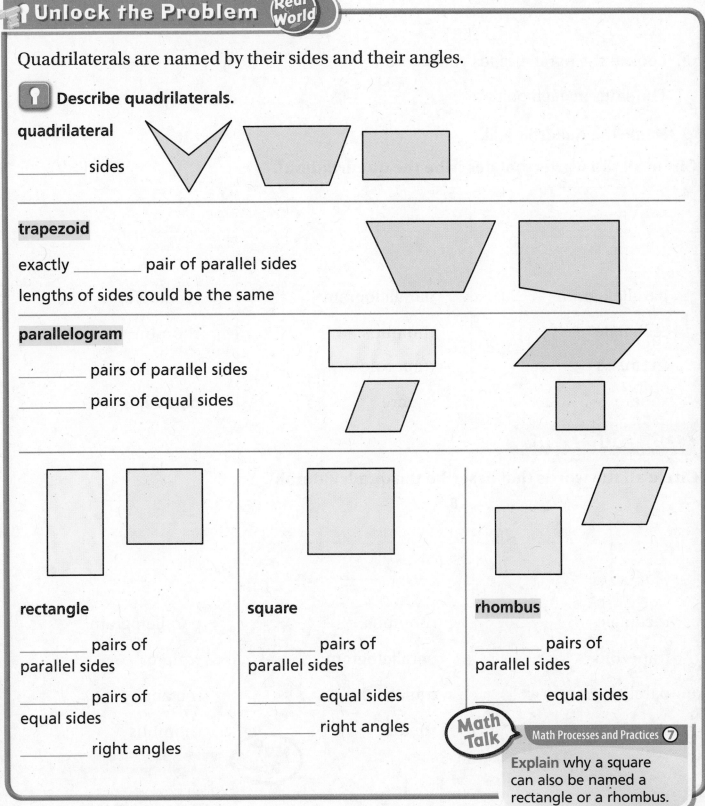

quadrilateral

_____ sides

trapezoid

exactly _____ pair of parallel sides

lengths of sides could be the same

parallelogram

_____ pairs of parallel sides

_____ pairs of equal sides

rectangle

_____ pairs of parallel sides

_____ pairs of equal sides

_____ right angles

square

_____ pairs of parallel sides

_____ equal sides

_____ right angles

rhombus

_____ pairs of parallel sides

_____ equal sides

Math Talk

Math Processes and Practices 7

Explain why a square can also be named a rectangle or a rhombus.

Look at the quadrilateral at the right.

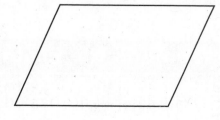

1. Outline each pair of parallel sides with a different color. How many pairs of sides appear to be parallel?

   _____

2. Look at the parallel sides you colored.

   The sides in each pair are _____.

3. Name the quadrilateral. _____

Circle all the words that describe the quadrilateral.

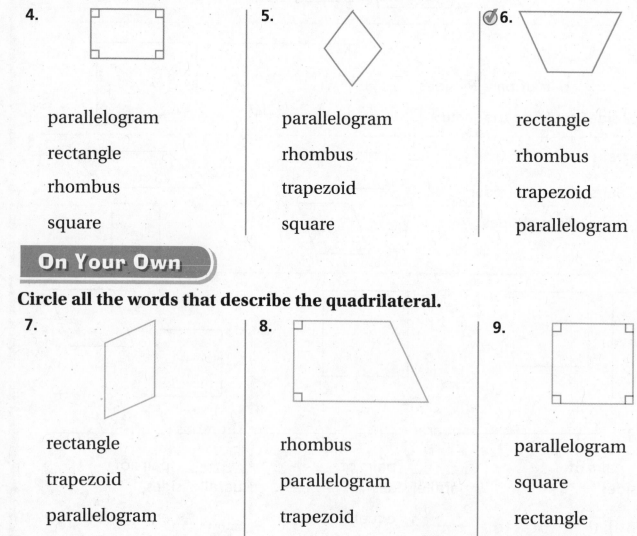

4.

parallelogram

rectangle

rhombus

square

5.

parallelogram

rhombus

trapezoid

square

6.

rectangle

rhombus

trapezoid

parallelogram

Circle all the words that describe the quadrilateral.

7.

rectangle

trapezoid

parallelogram

rhombus

8.

rhombus

parallelogram

trapezoid

square

9.

parallelogram

square

rectangle

rhombus

Math Talk Math Processes and Practices 6

Explain how you can have a rhombus that is not a square.

Name _____

Use the quadrilaterals at the right for 10–12.

10. Which quadrilaterals appear to have 4 right angles?

_____

11. Which quadrilaterals appear to have 2 pairs of parallel sides?

_____

12. Which quadrilaterals appear to have no right angles?

_____

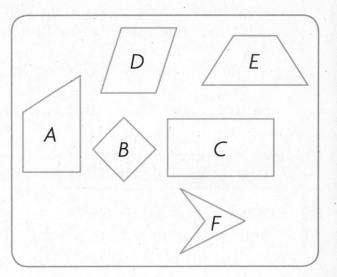

13. **WRITE** ▸*Math* **What's the Error?** Jacki drew the shape at the right. She said it is a parallelogram because it has 2 pairs of parallel sides. **Describe** her error.

_____

_____

_____

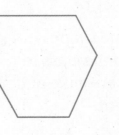

14. Circle the shape at the right that is not a quadrilateral. **Explain** your choice.

_____

_____

_____

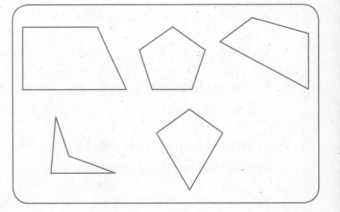

15. **GO DEEPER** I am a polygon that has 4 sides and 4 angles. At least one of my angles is acute. Circle all the shapes that I could be.

quadrilateral   parallelogram   rectangle

square   rhombus   trapezoid

16. **THINK SMARTER** Rita glued craft sticks together to make this shape. Which best describes the quadrilateral Rita made?

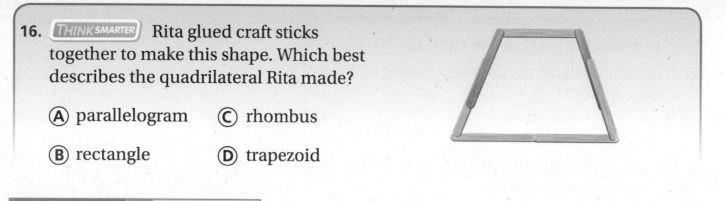

Ⓐ parallelogram   Ⓒ rhombus

Ⓑ rectangle   Ⓓ trapezoid

Connect to Reading

Compare and Contrast

When you *compare,* you look for ways that things are alike. When you *contrast,* you look for ways that things are different.

Mr. Briggs drew some shapes on the board. He asked the class to tell how the shapes are alike and how they are different.

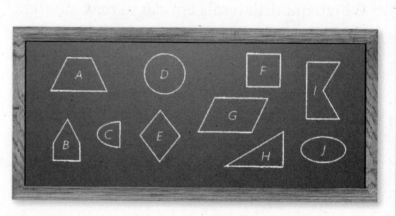

Complete the sentences.

- Shapes _____, _____, and _____ are not polygons.

- Shapes _____, _____, _____, and _____ are quadrilaterals.

- Shapes _____, _____, and _____ have only 1 pair of parallel sides.

- Shapes _____, _____, and _____ have 2 pairs of parallel sides.

- All four sides of shapes _____ and _____ appear to be the same length.

- In these shapes, the sides do not appear to be the same length. _____

- These shapes can be called rhombuses. _____

- Shape _____ is a parallelogram, but cannot be called a rhombus.

- Shape _____ is a parallelogram and can be called a square.

Classify Quadrilaterals

Learning Objective You will describe, classify, and compare quadrilaterals based on sides and angles.

Circle all the words that describe the quadrilateral.

1.

(parallelogram)

rectangle

rhombus

trapezoid

2.

parallelogram

rectangle

rhombus

trapezoid

3.

square

rectangle

rhombus

trapezoid

Use the quadrilaterals below for 4–6.

A   B   C   D   E

4. Which quadrilateral(s) appear to have only 1 pair of parallel sides?

_____

5. Which quadrilateral(s) appear to have 4 right angles?

_____

6. Which quadrilateral(s) appear to have 4 equal sides?

_____

Problem Solving

7. A picture on the wall in Jeremy's class has 4 right angles, 4 equal sides, and 2 pairs of parallel sides. What word best describes the picture?

_____

8. **WRITE** ▸ *Math* Explain how a trapezoid and rectangle are different.

_____

_____

_____

Lesson Check

1. Which name describes the quadrilateral?

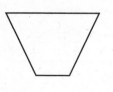

   A) square
   B) trapezoid
   C) rhombus
   D) rectangle

2. Which quadrilaterals appear to have 2 pairs of parallel sides?

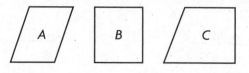

   A) *A* and *B*
   B) *A*, *B*, and *C*
   C) *A*
   D) *B*

Spiral Review

3. Which number will complete the number sentences?

   $5 \times \blacksquare = 35$

   $35 \div 5 = \blacksquare$

   A) 5   C) 7
   B) 6   D) 8

4. Divide.

   $48 \div 6$

   A) 8
   B) 9
   C) 10
   D) 11

5. Jen says that $\frac{4}{5}$ of the students in her class are wearing the color blue. Which fraction describes the number of students not wearing blue?

   _____

6. How many right angles does the shape appear to have?

   _____

Name _____

Draw Quadrilaterals

Essential Question How can you draw quadrilaterals?

Learning Objective You will use grid paper to draw and name quadrilaterals and then draw polygons that do not belong in a set of quadrilaterals and explain why.

⚷ Unlock the Problem

CONNECT You have learned to classify quadrilaterals by the number of pairs of opposite sides that are parallel, by the number of pairs of sides of equal length, and by the number of right angles.

How can you draw quadrilaterals?

🔓 Activity 1 Use grid paper to draw quadrilaterals.

Materials ■ ruler

- Use a ruler to draw line segments from points A to B, from B to C, from C to D, and from D to A.

- Write the name of your quadrilateral.

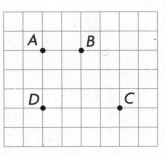

_____

🔓 Activity 2 Draw a shape that does not belong.

Materials ■ ruler

Ⓐ Here are three examples of a quadrilateral. Draw an example of a polygon that is not a quadrilateral.

- Explain why your polygon is not a quadrilateral.

_____

_____

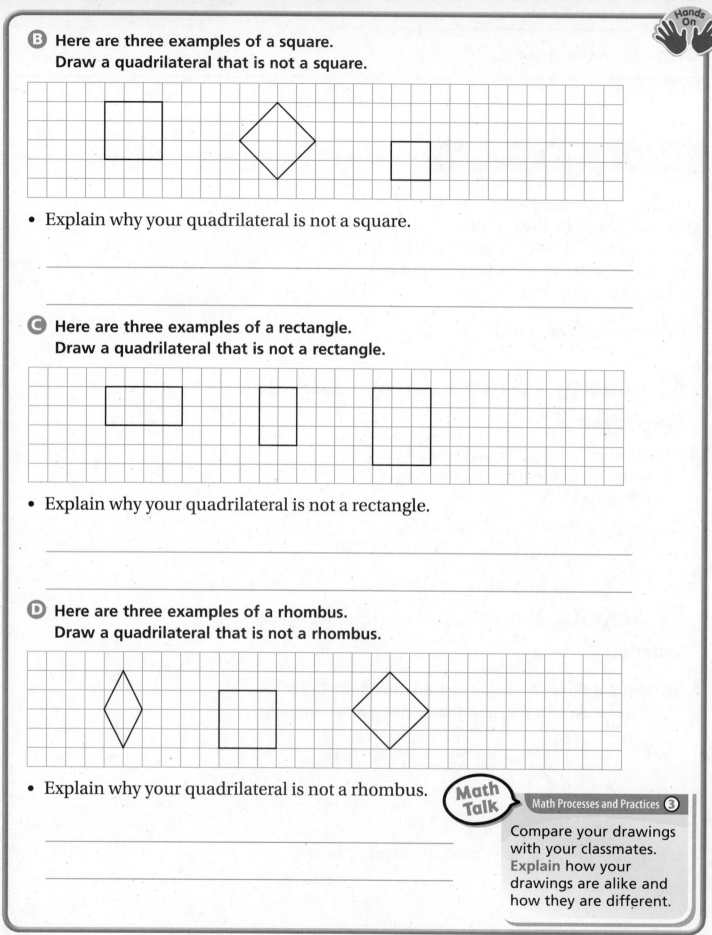

B Here are three examples of a square.
Draw a quadrilateral that is not a square.

- Explain why your quadrilateral is not a square.

_____

_____

C Here are three examples of a rectangle.
Draw a quadrilateral that is not a rectangle.

- Explain why your quadrilateral is not a rectangle.

_____

_____

D Here are three examples of a rhombus.
Draw a quadrilateral that is not a rhombus.

- Explain why your quadrilateral is not a rhombus.

Math Talk

Math Processes and Practices **3**

Compare your drawings with your classmates. **Explain** how your drawings are alike and how they are different.

_____

_____

Name _____

1. Choose 4 endpoints that connect to make a rectangle.

   Think: A rectangle has 2 pairs of opposite sides that are parallel, 2 pairs of sides of equal length, and 4 right angles.

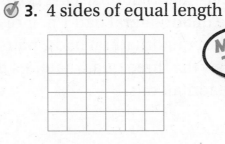

Draw a quadrilateral that is described. Name the quadrilateral you drew.

✓ 2. 2 pairs of equal sides

name _____

✓ 3. 4 sides of equal length

name _____

Math Talk

Math Processes and Practices ⑥

Explain one way the quadrilaterals you drew are alike and one way they are different.

On Your Own

Practice: Copy and Solve Use grid paper to draw a quadrilateral that is described. Name the quadrilateral you drew.

4. exactly 1 pair of opposite sides that are parallel

5. 2 pairs of parallel sides and 2 pairs of equal sides

6. 2 pairs of sides of equal length

Draw a quadrilateral that does not belong. Then explain why.

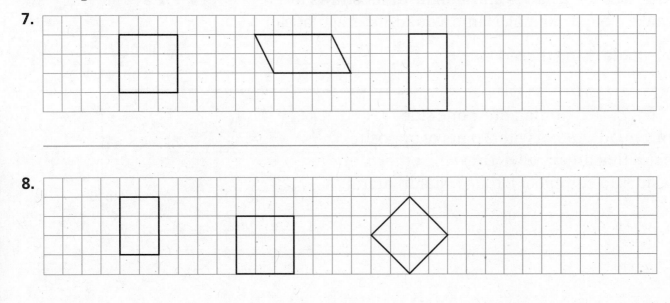

7.

8.

Problem Solving • Applications Real World

9. **Math Processes and Practices ③ Make Arguments** Jacki drew the shape at the right. She said it is a rectangle because it has 2 pairs of opposite sides that are parallel. Describe her error.

_____

_____

10. **GO DEEPER** Adam drew three quadrilaterals. One quadrilateral had no pairs of parallel sides, one quadrilateral had 1 pair of opposite sides that are parallel, and the last quadrilateral had 2 pairs of opposite sides that are parallel. Draw the three quadrilaterals that Adam could have drawn. Name the quadrilaterals.

_____   _____   _____

11. **THINK SMARTER** Amy has 4 straws of equal length. Name the quadrilaterals that can be made using these 4 straws.

_____ Amy cuts one of the straws in half. She uses the 2 halves and 2 of the other straws to make a quadrilateral. Name a quadrilateral that can

be made using these 4 straws. _____

12. **THINK SMARTER** Jordan drew one side of a quadrilateral with 2 pairs of opposite sides that are parallel. Draw the other 3 sides to complete Jordan's quadrilateral.

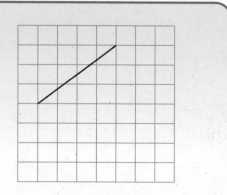

Draw Quadrilaterals

Learning Objective You will use grid paper to draw and name quadrilaterals and then draw polygons that do not belong in a set of quadrilaterals and explain why.

Draw a quadrilateral that is described. Name the quadrilateral you drew.

1. 4 sides of equal length

_____ square _____

2. 1 pair of opposite sides that are parallel

_____

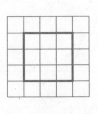 Problem Solving (Real World)

3. Layla drew a quadrilateral with 4 right angles and 2 pairs of opposite sides that are parallel. Name the quadrilateral she could have drawn.

_____

4. Victor drew a quadrilateral with no right angles and 4 sides of equal length. What quadrilateral could Victor have drawn?

_____

5. WRITE ▸Math Draw a quadrilateral that does not belong. Then explain why.

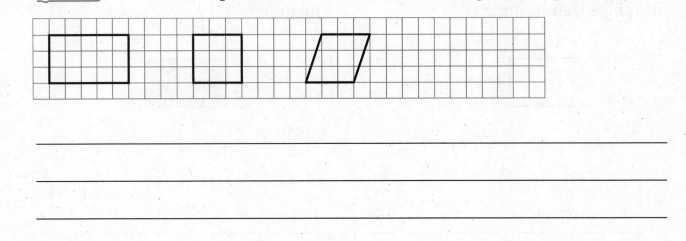

_____

_____

Lesson Check

1. Chloe drew a quadrilateral with 2 pairs of opposite sides that are parallel. Name a shape that could be Chloe's quadrilateral?

_____

_____

2. Mike drew a quadrilateral with 4 right angles. What shape could he have drawn?

_____

_____

Spiral Review

3. A quadrilateral has 2 pairs of parallel sides and 2 pairs of equal sides. What is the name of the quadrilateral?

_____

4. Mark drew 2 lines that form a right angle. What word describes the lines Mark drew?

_____

5. Dennis drew the rectangle on grid paper. What is the perimeter of the rectangle Dennis drew?

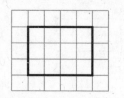

6. Jill drew the rectangle on grid paper. What is the area of the rectangle Jill drew?

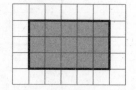

_____

_____

Problem Solving • Classify Plane Shapes

Essential Question How can you use the strategy *draw a diagram* to classify plane shapes?

Learning Objective You will use the strategy *draw a diagram* to classify plane shapes by using a Venn diagram.

🔑 Unlock the Problem (Real World)

A **Venn diagram** shows how sets of things are related. In the Venn diagram at the right, one circle has shapes that are rectangles. Shapes that are rhombuses are in the other circle. The shapes in the section where the circles overlap are both rectangles and rhombuses.

What type of quadrilateral is in both circles?

Rectangles   Rhombuses

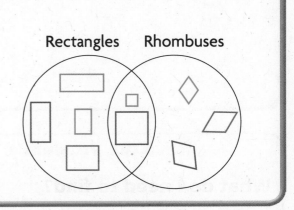

Read the Problem	Solve the Problem
What do I need to find? _____ _____	What is true about all quadrilaterals? _____ Which quadrilaterals have 2 pairs of opposite sides that are parallel? _____
What information do I need to use? the circles labeled _____ and _____	Which quadrilaterals have 4 sides of equal length? _____ Which quadrilaterals have 4 right angles? _____
How will I use the information? _____ _____	The quadrilaterals in the section where the circles overlap have _____ pairs of opposite sides that are parallel, _____ sides of equal length, and _____ right angles. So, _____ are in both circles.

Math Talk   Math Processes and Practices ⑥

Does a ▱ fit in the Venn diagram? **Explain.**

⬤ Try Another Problem

The Venn diagram shows the shapes Andrea used to make a picture. Where would the shape shown below be placed in the Venn diagram?

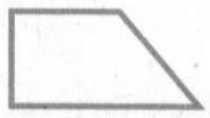

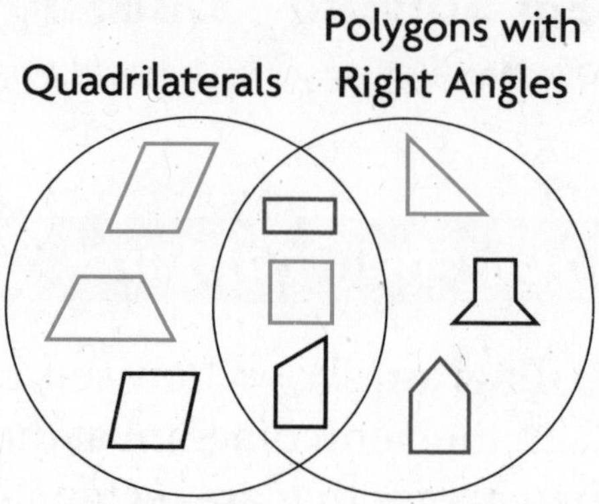

Quadrilaterals   Polygons with Right Angles

Read the Problem	Solve the Problem
What do I need to find?	**Record the steps you used to solve the problem.**
What information do I need to use?	
How will I use the information?	

1. How many shapes do not have right angles?

   _____

2. How many red shapes have right angles but are

   not quadrilaterals? _____

3. **Math Processes and Practices ②** **Reason Abstractly** What is a different way to sort the shapes?

   _____

   _____

Math Talk

Math Processes and Practices ⑥

What name can be used to describe all the shapes in the Venn diagram? **Explain** how you know.

© Houghton Mifflin Harcourt Publishing Company

Name _____

Use the Venn diagram for 1–3.

1. Jordan is sorting the shapes at the right in a Venn diagram. Where does the ◇ go?

   First, look at the sides and angles of the polygons.

   Next, draw the polygons in the Venn diagram.

   The shape has _____ sides of equal length

   and _____ right angles.

   So, the shape goes in the

   _____.

2. Where would you place a ⬡?

   _____

3. What if Jordan sorted the shapes by Polygons with Right Angles and Polygons with Angles Less Than a Right Angle? Would the circles still overlap? Explain.

   _____

   _____

4. **GO DEEPER** Eva drew the Venn diagram below. What labels could she have used for the diagram?

   _____   _____

   _____   _____

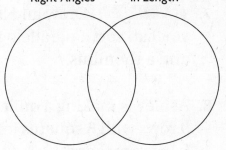

Polygons with Right Angles   Polygons with All Sides Equal in Length

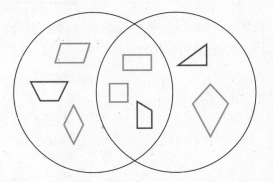

On Your Own

5. Ben and Marta are both reading the same book. Ben has read $\frac{1}{3}$ of the book. Marta has read $\frac{1}{4}$ of the book. Who has read more? _____

6. **Math Processes and Practices** ② **Represent a Problem** There are 42 students from 6 different classes in the school spelling bee. Each class has the same number of students in the spelling bee. Use the bar model to find how many students are from each class.

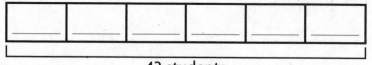

42 students

_____ students ÷ _____ classes = _____ students

7. THINK SMARTER   Draw and label a Venn diagram to show one way you can sort a parallelogram, a rectangle, a square, a trapezoid, and a rhombus.

8. Ashley is making a quilt with squares of fabric. There are 9 rows with 8 squares in each row. How many squares of fabric are there?

_____

9. THINK SMARTER   Sketch where to place these shapes in the Venn diagram.

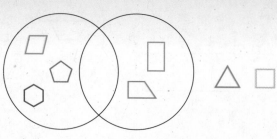

Polygons with All Sides
of Equal Length

Quadrilaterals with
Right Angles

Problem Solving • Classify Plane Shapes

Learning Objective You will use the strategy *draw a diagram* to classify plane shapes by using a Venn diagram.

Solve each problem.

1. Steve drew the shapes below. Write the letter of each shape where it belongs in the Venn diagram.

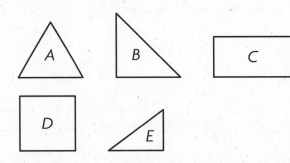

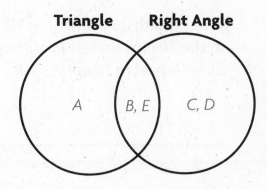

2. Janice drew the shapes below. Write the letter of each shape where it belongs in the Venn diagram.

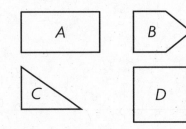

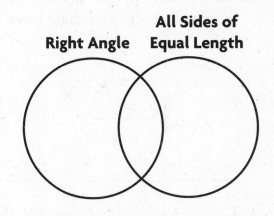

3. Beth drew the shapes below. Write the letter of each shape where it belongs in the Venn diagram.

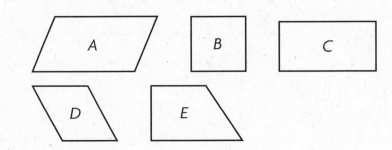

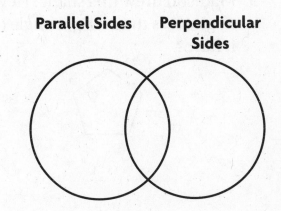

Lesson Check

1. What shape would go in the section where the two circles overlap?

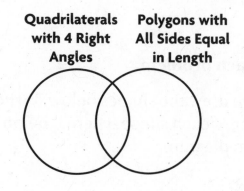

Quadrilaterals with 4 Right Angles   Polygons with All Sides Equal in Length

_____

2. What quadrilateral could NEVER go in the circle labeled *Polygons with All Sides Equal in Length?*

_____

Spiral Review

3. How many angles greater than a right angle does this triangle have?

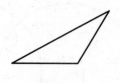

_____

4. How many sides of equal length does this triangle appear to have?

_____

5. Madison drew this shape. How many angles less than a right angle does it have?

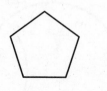

6. How many dots are in $\frac{1}{2}$ of this group?

. . . . . .

. . . . . .

. . . . . .

_____

_____

Name _____

Combine and Separate Plane Shapes

Essential Question How can you combine and separate plane shapes to make new shapes?

Learning Objective You will combine and separate plane shapes.

Unlock the Problem *Real World*

Activity 1

Materials ■ pattern blocks, MathBoard

Combine the pattern blocks to make different shapes. Trace the shapes.

A Combine two triangle pattern blocks to make a new shape. Trace the shape.

B Combine two blue rhombus pattern blocks to make a new shape. Trace the shape.

C Combine the two rhombus pattern blocks another way to make a new shape. Trace the shape.

D On your MathBoard, combine other pattern blocks to make new shapes.

1. Look at the shapes you made in A–D. Name as many shapes as you can.

   _____

   _____

2. On your MathBoard, combine six triangle pattern blocks to make a hexagon. Then combine the same pattern blocks to make a different shape. Trace both shapes on your MathBoard.

Math Talk

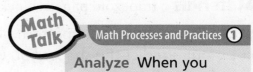

Math Processes and Practices ①

Analyze When you combine two triangles, why do you always form a quadrilateral?

CONNECT You have learned how to combine plane shapes to make other shapes. You can also take apart, or separate, plane shapes to make different shapes.

Activity 2

Materials ■ pattern blocks, scissors, paper

You can cut plane shapes apart to make different shapes.

STEP 1 On another sheet of paper, trace a square pattern block twice. Cut the two shapes out.

STEP 2 Fold one square in half so that two vertices are on the fold. Cut the shape along the fold. Trace the new shapes.

STEP 3 Now, fold the other square in half so that the middle of two sides is on the fold. Cut the shape along the fold. Trace the new shapes.

You can make new shapes by drawing diagonals in plane shapes. A **diagonal** is a line segment that connects two vertices of a polygon that are not next to each other. What new shape do you see in this square?

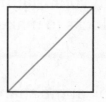

Try This!

Materials ■ trapezoid pattern block, scissors, paper

STEP 1 Trace a trapezoid pattern block and cut it out. Predict the shapes you will have if you draw a diagonal line in your trapezoid.

STEP 2 Test your prediction by drawing the diagonal and then cutting the shape along the diagonal. What new shapes do you have? Was your prediction correct?

Name _____

**Name a new shape that can be made by combining
two of the pattern block shapes shown.**

1.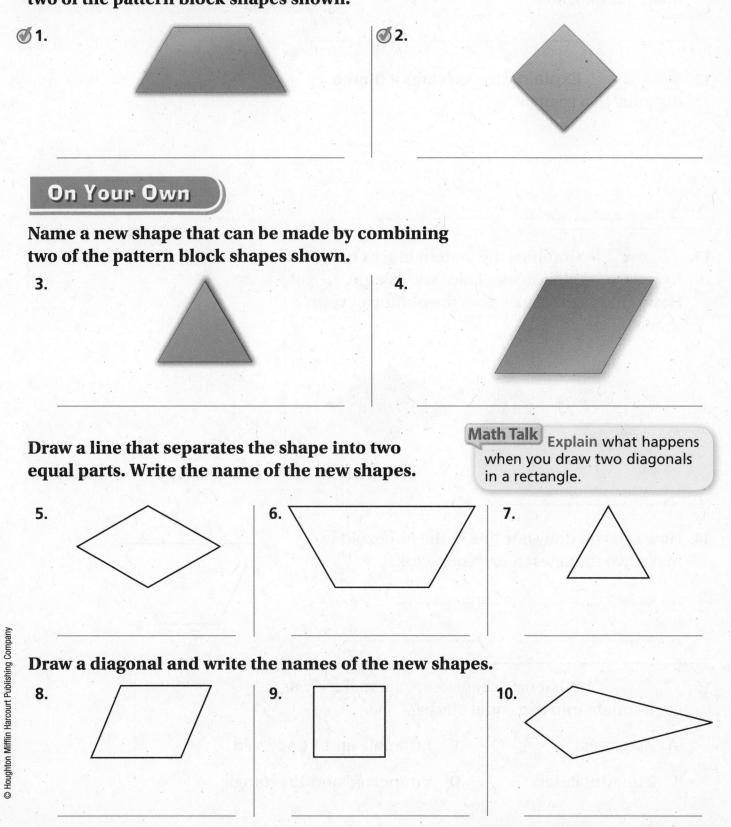

_____

2.

_____

**Name a new shape that can be made by combining
two of the pattern block shapes shown.**

3.

_____

4.

_____

**Draw a line that separates the shape into two
equal parts. Write the name of the new shapes.**

Math Talk Explain what happens
when you draw two diagonals
in a rectangle.

5.

_____

6.

_____

7.

_____

Draw a diagonal and write the names of the new shapes.

8.

_____

9.

_____

10.

_____

Problem Solving • Applications (Real World)

11. Carter has green triangle pattern blocks. How many of his blocks will it take to make 3 trapezoids?

_____

12. **THINK SMARTER** **Explain** why you cannot draw a diagonal in a triangle.

_____

_____

_____

13. **THINK SMARTER** Combine the pattern blocks below to make a 7-sided shape. Trace your shape. How many right angles does the outline of your shape have?

_____

14. How can you draw one line in the trapezoid to make two triangles? Show your work.

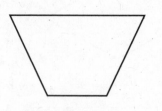

_____

_____

15. **THINK SMARTER** What new shapes can you make if you cut a square into two equal pieces?

(A) 2 squares   (B) 1 triangle and 1 trapezoid

(C) 2 quadrilaterals   (D) 1 trapezoid and 1 rectangle

Combine and Separate Plane Shapes

Name a new shape that can be made by combining two of the pattern block shapes shown.

1.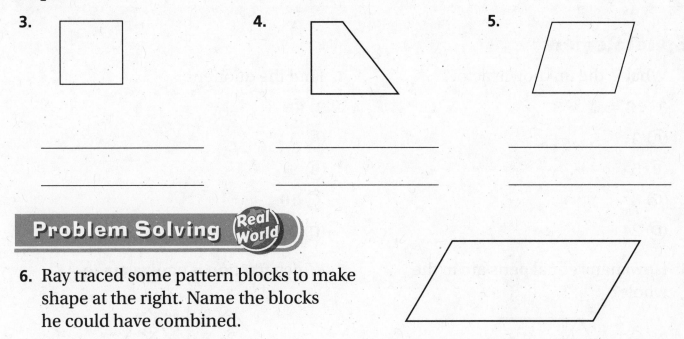
   _____

2.
   _____

Draw a diagonal and write the names of the new shapes.

3.
   _____

   _____

4.
   _____

   _____

5.
   _____

   _____

Problem Solving Real World

6. Ray traced some pattern blocks to make shape at the right. Name the blocks he could have combined.

_____

_____

_____

Lesson Check

1. Which shape can be made by combining the pattern blocks shown?

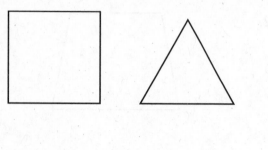

(A) rhombus   (C) pentagon

(B) trapezoid   (D) hexagon

2. Samuel cut this shape on a diagonal. What shapes did he make?

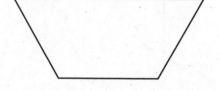

(A) 2 triangles   (C) 2 rhombuses

(B) 2 rectangles   (D) 2 trapezoids

Spiral Review

3. What is the unknown factor?

$3 \times 8 = \blacksquare \times 3$

(A) 3

(B) 5

(C) 8

(D) 24

4. Find the quotient.

$3\overline{)30}$

(A) 3

(B) 9

(C) 10

(D) 30

5. How many equal parts are in the whole?

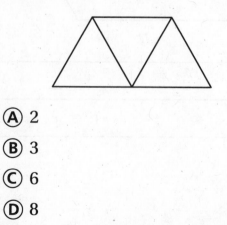

(A) 2

(B) 3

(C) 6

(D) 8

6. Which fraction is equivalent to $\frac{4}{10}$?

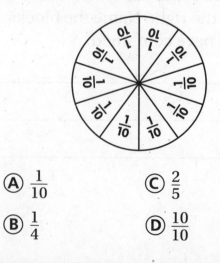

(A) $\frac{1}{10}$ (C) $\frac{2}{5}$

(B) $\frac{1}{4}$ (D) $\frac{10}{10}$

Name _____

Identify Congruent Shapes

Essential Question How can you identify two-dimensional shapes that are congruent?

Unlock the Problem *Real World*

Shapes that have the same size and the same shape are **congruent**.

Look at the traffic signs at the right. Do the signs appear to be congruent?

🔑 **Compare size and shape.**

These pairs of shapes appear to be congruent.

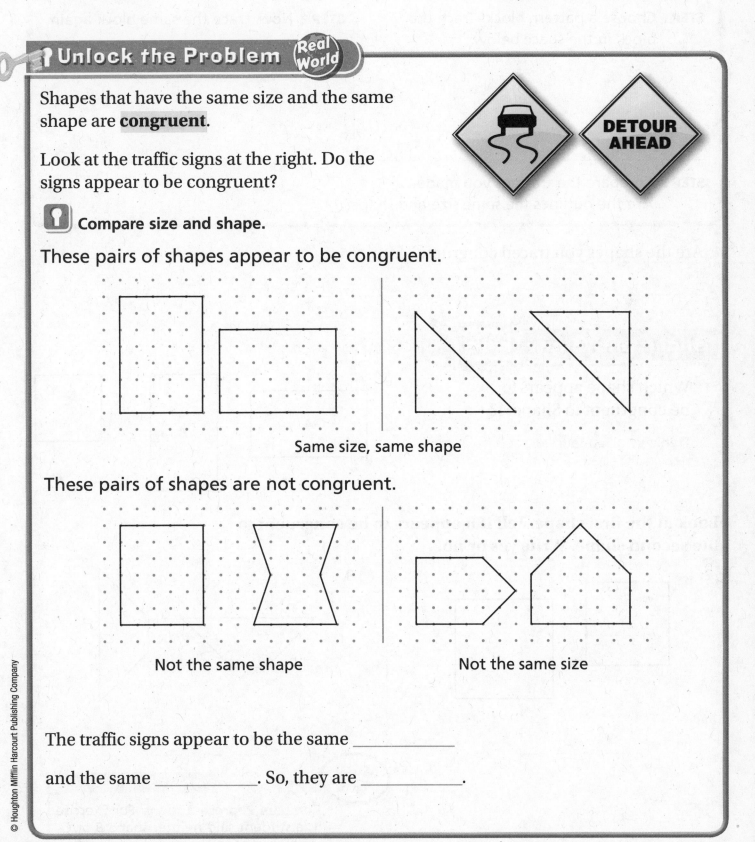

Same size, same shape

These pairs of shapes are not congruent.

Not the same shape   Not the same size

The traffic signs appear to be the same _____

and the same _____. So, they are _____.

Materials ▪ pattern blocks ▪ paper

Trace pattern blocks to find congruent shapes.

STEP 1 Choose a pattern block. Trace the block in the space below.

STEP 2 Now, trace the same block again.

STEP 3 Compare the tracings you made. Are the outlines the same size and shape? _____

● Are the shapes you traced congruent? **Explain.**

Share and Show MATH BOARD

1. Which shape appears to be congruent to Shape A?

   Think: Which quadrilateral is the same size and shape?

Look at the first shape. Tell if it appears to be congruent to the second shape. Write yes or no.

2.

3.

Math Talk

Math Processes and Practices ③

Compare Representations For Exercise 1, a student said neither shape B or C is congruent to shape A. Explain why the student might think this.

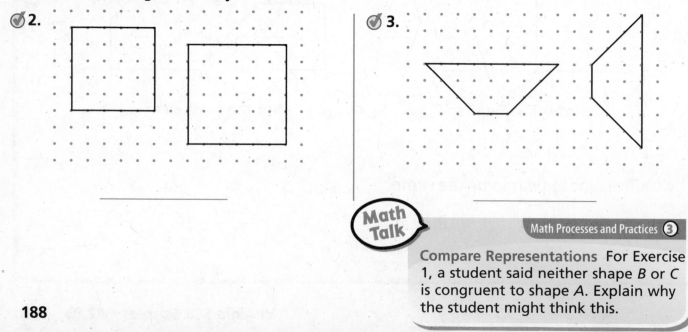

Name _____

On Your Own

Look at the first shape. Tell if it appears to be congruent to the second shape. Write *yes* or *no*.

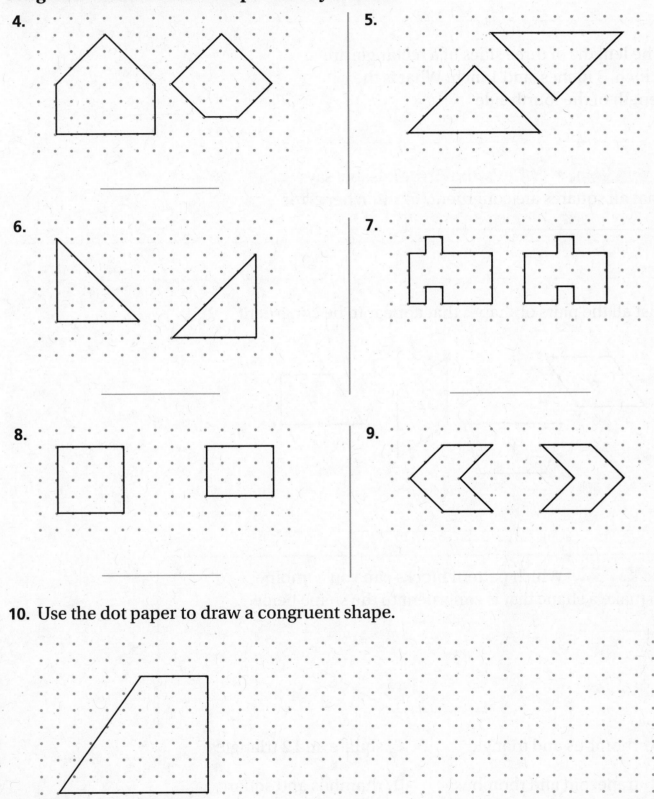

4. _____

5. _____

6. _____

7. _____

8. _____

9. _____

10. Use the dot paper to draw a congruent shape.

© Houghton Mifflin Harcourt Publishing Company

Virginia SOL Success • 12.9b   189

Problem Solving • Applications (Real World)

11. **THINK SMARTER** What two congruent shapes can you combine to make a hexagon?

_____

12. The lengths of three sides of a rectangle are 1 inch, 3 inches, and 1 inch. What is the length of the fourth side?

_____

13. **Write Math** ▶ **What's the Error?** Isabel says that all squares are congruent. **Explain** her error.

_____

_____

14. List all the pairs of shapes that appear to be congruent.

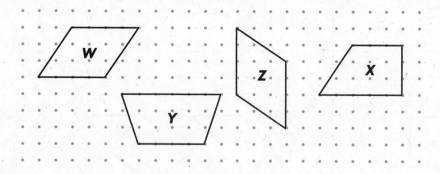

_____

15. **THINK SMARTER** Which pattern blocks can you combine to make a shape that is congruent to the shape below?

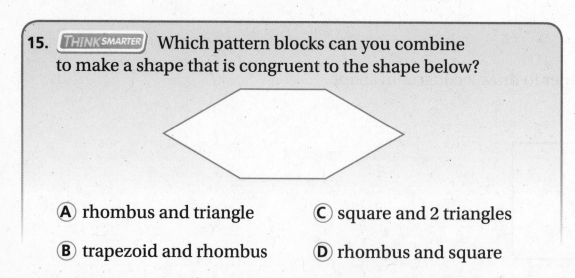

(A) rhombus and triangle   (C) square and 2 triangles

(B) trapezoid and rhombus   (D) rhombus and square

Identify Congruent Shapes

Learning Objective You will identify and draw congruent shapes.

Look at the first shape. Tell if it appears to be congruent to the second shape. Write *yes* or *no*.

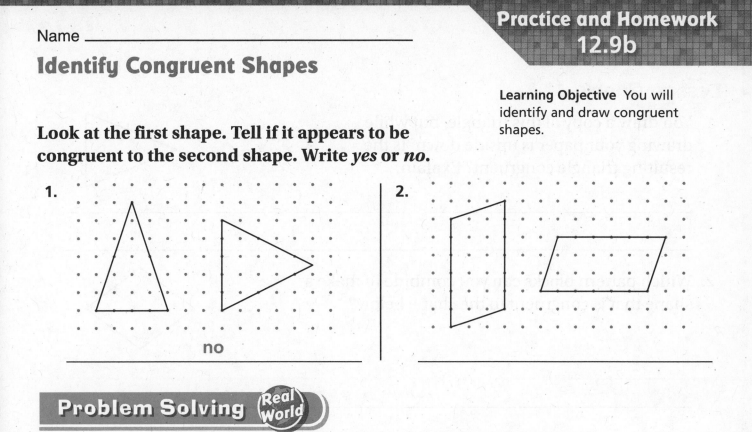

1.

no

2.

Problem Solving Real World

3. The lengths of three sides of a parallelogram are 2 inches, 5 inches, and 2 inches. What is the length of the fourth side?

_____

4. List all the pairs of shapes that appear to be congruent.

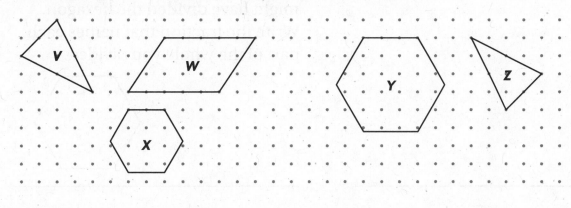

_____

5. **WRITE** *Math* Draw two shapes that are congruent. Then draw two shapes that are not congruent. Explain both sets of drawings.

_____

_____

Lesson Check

1. You draw a copy of this triangle, but while drawing your paper is upside down. Is the resulting triangle congruent? Explain.

_____

_____

2. Which pattern blocks can you combine to make a shape that is congruent to the shape below?

_____

Spiral Review

3. How many triangle pattern blocks do you need to make a trapezoid?

_____

4. Kawan divided a hexagon into 3 congruent parts. Show how he might have divided the hexagon. Write the fraction that names each part of the whole you divided.

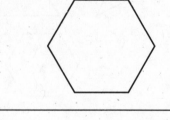

_____

5. Ronald is making punch for a party. He mixes together 2 gallons of cranberry juice and 3 gallons of grape juice in a 10-gallon bowl. How much more punch can the bowl hold?

_____

6. Maria buys two dozen bagels. She wants to divide the bagels equally between her 8 friends. How many bagels will each of her friends get?

_____

Name _____

Patterns with Shapes and Objects

Essential Question How can you use plane shapes to find patterns?

CONNECT You can use what you know about plane shapes to describe, extend, and create shape patterns.

Learning Objective You will describe, extend, and create repeating and growing patterns.

Unlock the Problem *Real World*

You can see patterns in everyday objects and shapes. You can use shape, size, position, color, or number of shapes to describe what changes from one shape to the next in a pattern.

Look for a pattern. Find a pattern core, and then draw the next two shapes.

Think: What part of the pattern repeats? _____

• What if there was a hexagon after each square?
  Draw what the pattern core would look like.

Try This! **Describe a pattern. Draw the next two shapes in the growing pattern below.**

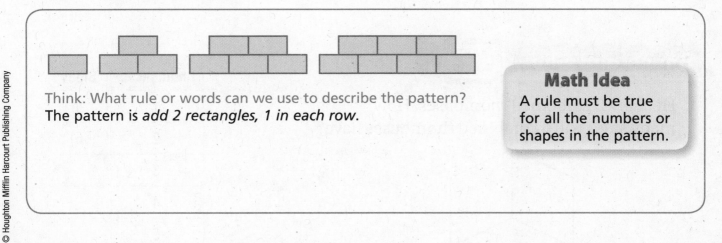

Think: What rule or words can we use to describe the pattern?
The pattern is *add 2 rectangles, 1 in each row*.

Math Idea
A rule must be true for all the numbers or shapes in the pattern.

© Houghton Mifflin Harcourt Publishing Company

1 Activity   **Materials** ■ trapezoid pattern block

Use pattern blocks to show a pattern.

STEP 1 Trace a trapezoid pattern block and record the number of sides.

STEP 2 To the right of the trapezoid you traced, trace the pattern block again, and record the total number of sides.

STEP 3 Continue to trace until you have combined four trapezoid pattern blocks without overlapping. Record the number of sides in the new shape.

STEP 4 List the number of trapezoids and the number of sides in the table below. Describe the pattern.

_____

_____

Trapezoids	Sides
1	4
2	6
3	
4	

- What if you traced and combined 7 trapezoid pattern blocks? How many sides will there be? How do you know?

Math Talk

Math Processes and Practices ②

Use Reasoning Explain how you know your description is correct.

_____

_____

Share and Show   MATH BOARD

1. Here are 2 combined rhombuses. How many sides will 5 combined rhombuses have? _____

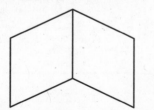

Rhombuses	Sides
1	4
2	6
3	
4	
5	

Name _____

2. Write the pattern core. Draw the next shape.

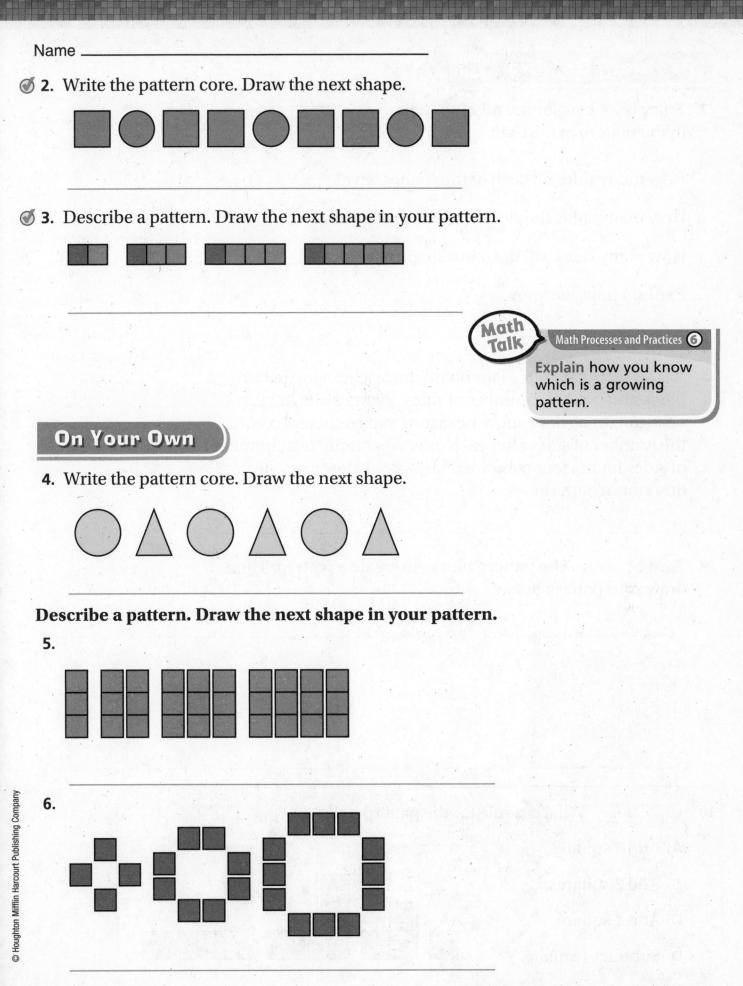

_____

3. Describe a pattern. Draw the next shape in your pattern.

_____

Math Talk

Math Processes and Practices ⑥

Explain how you know which is a growing pattern.

On Your Own

4. Write the pattern core. Draw the next shape.

_____

Describe a pattern. Draw the next shape in your pattern.

5.

_____

6.

_____

Problem Solving Real World

7. Tracy is looking for the missing shape
in the pattern at the right.

How many sides do each of the shapes have? _____

How many sides should the missing shape have? _____

How many sides will the tenth shape have? _____

Explain how you know. _____

_____

8. **THINK SMARTER** On your Math Board, trace a hexagon pattern
block and write the number of sides. Right beside the first
hexagon, trace three more hexagons and count and record
the number of sides after each one. What is the total number
of sides for the four combined hexagons? How can you
describe, a pattern?

_____

9. **WRITE** ▸*Math* Use pattern blocks to create a pattern. Then
draw your pattern below.

10. **THINK SMARTER** What is a rule for the pattern below?

Ⓐ Add 3 squares.

Ⓑ Add 2 squares.

Ⓒ Add 1 square.

Ⓓ Subtract 1 square.

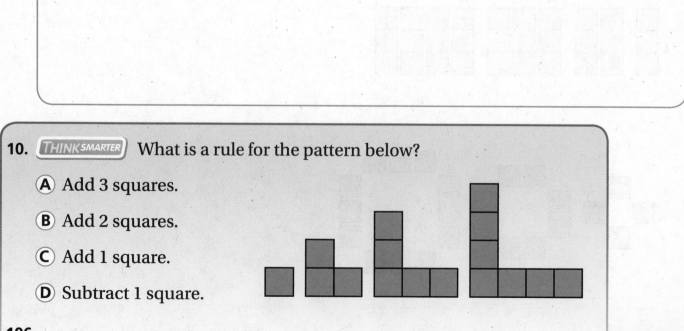

Algebra • Patterns with Shapes and Objects

Learning Objective You will describe, extend, and create repeating and growing patterns.

Write the pattern core or describe a pattern.

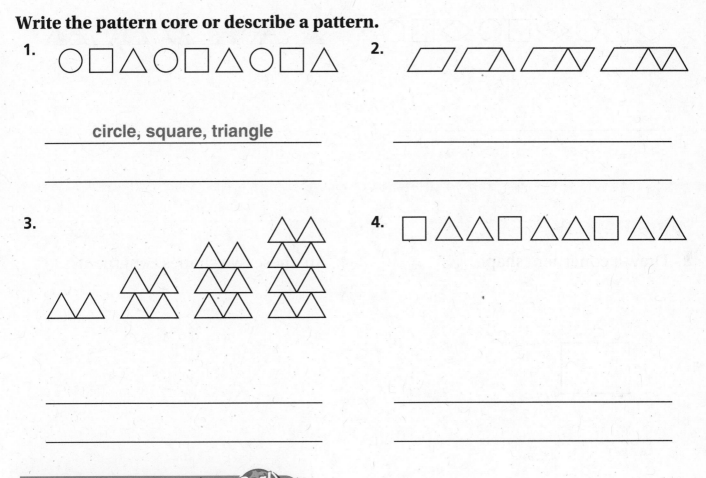

1. _____
   circle, square, triangle
   _____

2. _____
   _____

3. _____
   _____

4. _____
   _____

Problem Solving *Real World*

5. A growing pattern has 2 triangles, then 4 triangles, then 6 triangles, then 8 triangles. What rule can you use to describe a pattern?

   _____

6. Draw a repeating pattern using a square and a triangle.

Lesson Check

1. Find the pattern core. Draw and name the next shape.

_____

2. Look at the pattern. What rule describes a pattern?

_____

Spiral Review

3. Draw a congruent shape.

4. Are these two shapes congruent?

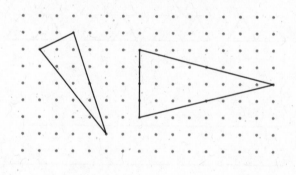

_____

5. Draw a diagonal and write the name of the new shapes.

6. Name a line segment.

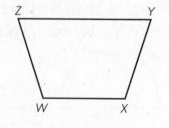

_____